Dogs and Ducks and Hat-Rack Bucks

...short stories for the outdoorsman

Larry Dablemont

Illustrations by Tom Goldsmith

**Lightnin'
Ridge Books**

Box 22
Bolivar • MO 65613

REVISED EDITION • SECOND PRINTING

Dogs and Ducks and Hat-Rack Bucks
...short stories for the outdoorsman

Copyright 1999 by Larry Dablemont

Published by:
Lightnin' Ridge Books
Box 22 • Bolivar, MO 65613 • USA

Illustrations:
Tom Goldsmith

Editing:
Mary Beth Vance

Design:
• Peggy Wells

ISBN: 0-9673975-2-9

LIBRARY OF CONGRESS CATALOG NUMBER: 99-96997

TABLE OF CONTENTS

CHAPTER 1

The Hat-Rack Buck

He had grown some since the old man had seen him last. But little wonder, he was nearly 15 years old. It had been more than two years. Waiting at the bus station, the grandfather had been a little nervous, wondering what kind of young man his grandson had become. But by the time the luggage was packed into the old pickup, the ice had been broken. They had plenty of things to talk about as they bounced along the gravel road to the farm.

"Season opens Monday," the old man said "That means we've got a lot to do in only two days. But, I've got several good stands, an' the bucks are really in the rut .... we'll need to sharpen your shootin' eye a bit."

"I just couldn't believe it when Mom said I could miss a week of school to come up here," the boy said. "You must've had to do some real talkin'."

The old man laughed, "I told her I'd never bring her mother to the city again if she said no."

Supper was nearly ready for the table when they arrived and the boy's grandmother was waiting to greet her grandson, whom she hadn't seen in almost two years.

They talked late into the evening and afterwards the boy moved his luggage to an upstairs bedroom of the old two-story farmhouse. His grandmother brought out extra homemade quilts, ones he remembered from visits as a small boy.

"I expect it'll be good an' chilly while you're

1

here," she said. "Seems like we always have a cold snap during the deer season."

He was a city boy, this youngster. The only thing he knew that wasn't akin to suburbs and shopping centers was this old farm. And his Grandpa had tried to salvage the boy somewhat at a very young age, especially during summer vacations when there were opportunities to fish the river that bordered the farm and hunt squirrels with a 22. The boy was always a little worried that he wasn't quite measuring up to his Grandpa's expectations, but really, the old man was proud of him. He knew how tough it was for a boy to grow up without a father. He wished that there was some way that his daughter and grandson could move back to the country some day. He could even envision the farm belonging to this youngster in distant years.

At 14, the grandson couldn't imagine owning the farm, of course. In the quiet upstairs room, snuggled in the softness of the old feather bed, he drifted to sleep dreaming of bagging a giant buck, an accomplishment that would make his grandfather extra proud.

"Now boy, that is a big buck that made that track," the old man said, stooping to look hard at the place in the pond bank mud where the deer had watered. It was early Saturday morning, the frost yet to be scattered by the rising sun.

"Down that path a hunnerd yards there's a small

2

clearin' with a couple ol' apple trees. Used to be an ol' homestead there. On past it, the ground slopes off into a little crick valley that goes down to the river," the old man pointed his gnarled finger down a faint trail. The boy remembered the old homestead and the creek. Years ago they had hunted mushrooms there in the spring.

"I've got a tree stand built there in a big red oak at the edge of that little openin'," the old man said. "Your uncle hunted there last year an' got a nice buck, so I think it'd be your best spot. Deer cross that openin' from several directions, comin' to get those apples in the early fall, an' comin' up to this ol' pond an' salt lick. I've found some big scrapes and rubs around the edge of it, an' when the hunters get thick on the other side of the river, the bucks'll high-tail it across to the crick and right up through that clearin'. It's a real crossroads fer 'em."

The old man motioned the boy back to the pickup. "This evenin'," he said, "we'll go look your stand over some. Right now, we need to go check on some cattle, an' then we'll do some practice shootin' over at your uncle's place."

As they headed back through the pasture, the old man turned right, driving the pickup along a trail of a road that skirted a woodland border, then into a good-sized pasture. As they came into the clearing, surrounded by pine and hardwoods, they both spotted a doe and yearling moving back toward the other end of the pasture. The doe was a good-sized one and she nervously trotted toward the timber as the old man stopped the truck and turned off the ignition.

"We'll watch a minute," he said. "This time of year, a buck may be only a few minutes behind a doe, follerin' aroun' all lovesick an' dejected."

The boy smiled. "Maybe we'll see that buck that made those big tracks at the pond," he said.

The old man shook his head, "No, I don't spect so, that buck was Ol' Hat-rack I figger, an' he won't be comin' across that pasture; he'd skirt it.... prob'-ly never let us see him."

"Ol' Hat-rack?" the boy questioned.

"Yeah, that's what I call him," his grandfather replied, "course ever' real big buck in the country is called 'Ol Hat-rack,' so I figgered this'n deserved that title, too. He's got a heck of a set of antlers, an' one tine on his right side that has a little extra point near its top. That's how you can tell 'im, but law, son, you'd know him anyway. He looks like a horse in a deerskin - with a tall, heavy rack.

"Is he real old, Grandpa?" the boy asked.

"I reckon he is," the old hunter answered. "I saw him two or three year ago, and he was a dandy then. He'd always hot-foot it up here on the farm an' hole up in the sumac and cedar thickets after the first day or so of huntin' ...to get away from the hunters in the National Forest land across the river, and just cool his heels for a while. If he don't lose his head completely over some sweet young doe, you don't see him much after a day or so of the season. He gets to be a night-dweller."

Finally, the old man started the pickup and they continued on, the boy asking more questions about Ol' Hat-rack and his grandfather promising to show him solid proof of the giant deer.

That afternoon, they took down the worn .30-30 rifle, an old Savage single-shot that the old man had bought new right after World War II. The youth had heard many stories about the deer it had dropped over the years, including the only one his father had ever killed, sixteen years ago, just after he and the boy's mother were married. The old man didn't talk much about that but the antlers of that six-pointer were the only ones that had ever hung in the old farmhouse.

It didn't take long to see that the rifle's sights were on target and the boy didn't flinch against the recoil. After all, he had learned to shoot a shotgun when he was 12 years old. The rifle was nothing. And he wouldn't mention the soreness in his shoulder that night.

On Sunday, after church, they visited several tree stands so that the youngster would know where his uncle and grandfather would be hunting. The old man showed the boy how to use the rope to safely haul up his rifle and knapsack and showed him the trails where a buck likely would approach.

That night, with farm chores finished and supper over, the old man and his grandson built up a fire in the old stove and talked about the big buck. It was then that the old man brought out the antler he had found years before.

"He shed this in January, an' I found it 'fore the mice chewed it up completely," the grandfather told the boy. "Notice how that long tine hangs down there. Funny thing, ever' year it comes back just about like that."

"Do his antlers get bigger each year?" the youngster asked.

"Maybe a little, but not too much, I don't suppose," the old man said as he worked a twist of tobacco from a leather pouch. "But, they don't need to get no bigger. Onc't a couple years back he was in my sights fer a minute or more an' them antlers looked like a rockin' chair."

"Did you miss him?" the boy asked in disbelief.

"Naw, I didn't miss, I just couldn't shoot," his grandfather said, cutting a plug of tobacco, placing it in his mouth on the blade of his knife.

"I always want a deer to put in the freezer, an' heck, he wasn't gonna be the best eatin' deer in the woods." There was a pause, and the old man went on. "Well, mostly I just kinda feel like he oughta be left out there. He's a lot like me, that ol' buck, kind of an oddball maybe, but darned independent. Part of this farm is mine, belonged to my daddy, part of

7

it is his, and belonged to his daddy."

The fire popped in the stove and it was quiet but for the radio in the kitchen, where the youth's grandmother was finishing the dishes.

"I tell ya somethin' else boy," the old man went on. "I ain't never been much on trophies. Guys in town think the bigger the buck, the bigger man they are. I don't buy that. Every year, the bigger bucks are brought down and the scrawny ones passed up. Sooner or later, all you got to sire the new crop of fawns is a bunch of four- and five-year old forkhorns with antlers the size of your thumb."

"I like to think there's a bunch of nice bucks gonna be runnin' aroun' this farm for years to come because of that big fellow. Who knows, maybe you'll get one of 'em," the boy's grandfather finished.

The boy thought about what his grandfather had told him that night as he lay in his bed upstairs. He tried to remember everything he had been told about tree stands and rifle sights and bucks that materialize from nothing. When you're 14, you don't sleep much on the night before your first deer hunt... it seemed he had time to think about everything several times. And when he would drift off to sleep, eventually, he would dream of the buck with the hatrack antlers.

It is cold on a November deer stand at dawn and when there is no sign of deer, it can be difficult for a youngster to endure. There was no sun, not even

8

a hint of its rays in the east. The wind was notice-able and seemed to be picking up a bit. The boy rubbed his nose with his gloved hand, thinking to himself that he'd probably need that rain slicker in his pack.

An hour later a small doe trotted through the opening, not even stopping to look at the few decaying apples on the ground as she passed. She seemed intent on getting to the pond behind the boy and showed no sign of being aware of his presence.

For that reason, he watched the trail coming straight up the slope toward him with a special interest. He saw the deer as it approached, long before he could tell it was a buck. It was going to work perfectly, the boy was sure. He prayed he wouldn't begin to shake violently and scare the deer away. In very little time, the buck, with a nice set of antlers, walked to within 50 yards of the clearing and stopped, head high. The boy looked hard at the buck, wondering if he had seen him. But no, the deer wasn't looking at him. Maybe the buck would come closer.

It was then that the youngster saw the object of the eight-pointer's attention. Out of the corner of his eye the boy caught the movement in the trail to his left. He glanced toward the movement and his heart jumped to his throat. The hat-rack buck stood there, looking down the slope toward the first buck, nervously shaking that massive set of antlers, perhaps as a warning.

The big buck stepped forward cautiously as if issuing a challenge to the intruder. He was less than 25 yards away...it would be an easy shot. As the youngster moved the barrel ever so slowly he thought of his grandfather's words, "I ain't never been much on trophies . . . . I just kinda feel like he oughta be left out there... he's a lot like me, that old buck."

There was a rifle shot well off in the distance. Ignoring it, the first buck, head high and nostrils flared, walked forward on stiff legs! In the tree stand, the boy saw the huge buck moving closer. In the sights of his rifle was a buck like none other in the river valley, the buck of a lifetime. Glancing back down the slope, he noticed the eight-pointer was 15 yards closer.

The river valley echoed with a single shot. Back at the farmhouse, the boy's grandmother looked up from her job of scattering feed for a handful of chickens. Once again the rifle roared and then there was quiet as a cold mist began to fall.

In the light rain of mid-afternoon the old man pulled his pickup into the small-town service station and greeted the owner as he came out to fill the tank. As they lifted the hood the old man took the liberty of boasting a little.

"My grandson got his first deer this mornin', Ed," he said with a smile, "a dandy eight-pointer."

The station owner nodded his approval. "I already heard about that. Sounds like he's gonna be a hunter to be proud of."

"Gonna be?" the old hunter feigned indignation, "Heck, man, he already is!"

Back on the farm, Old Hat-rack moved slowly and cautiously into the cedar glade as the cold afternoon rain grew heavier. In the cedars, he would weather the rain and most of the deer season. Only he and the boy would ever know how close he had come to being a memory.

With a belligerent toss of his lowered head, the hat-rack buck ripped a small cedar with the massive set of antlers, then lifted his head high to gaze in the direction of the apple tree clearing and the empty tree stand in the red oak tree.

CHAPTER 2

First Mallard

The lights came on early in the old farmhouse and 13-year old Justin Surber was one of the first to rise. The family had arrived the day before from the city, for a weekend visit with Justin's grandparents. For the youngster the high point of the visit would be the duck hunting trip on Saturday morning.

But no one had counted on the cold snap. Uncle Verl settled at the breakfast table over a hot cup of coffee to break the bad news.

"Twenty-two degrees," he said, "never seen it this cold so early in the season. We ain't gonna be able to pull a boat into the blind. Shallow water is all froze over, decoys are gonna be iced in. We can break it up and have some huntin' I reckon, but it'll be work.... we'll hafta' wade in and break ice all the way."

Justin didn't care about the ice nor the cold. All he had thought about for two weeks was this hunting trip and no obstacle seemed too great. After all, Grandpa said the mallards were in and they had killed a limit on Thursday.

Unfortunately the ice and cold gave Justin's mother strong reservations and his father agreed. "You can't wade all the way to the blind, Son," he said, "it would be over your boots in some places. Maybe in the afternoon, after we clear a boat lane, we can take you back in."

As his grandmother set breakfast on the table before the men, Justin could have cried with very little effort. He just knew he could make it, but he also knew better than to argue the point with his father.

At the head of the table Justin's grandfather saw

the disappointment in the youngster's eyes. His sons had perhaps forgotten what such a hunting trip could mean to a boy. As they made plans, he shook his head.

"Too much work for me," the old man said as he poured gravy over biscuits. He caught Justin's eye, and winked. "I believe I'll let you two go ahead. Maybe the boy and I'll wait 'til it warms a bit an' then take a little trip down to the river."

Justin's mother joined the breakfast table discussion. In her robe and only half awake, she still objected because of the cold, but his father consented. "Dad and I used to float down that river and jump-shoot ducks when I was considerably younger than Justin," he said. "If you'll wait 'til the sun's up it'll warm up enough to tolerate."

Suddenly the despair lifted a little and the boy wished that sun-up was a little closer.

The temperature indeed had risen a bit when they drove down to the river over the frozen bottom-road. The sun's first rays were touching the treetops. An old johnboat waited, chained to a tree. The old man worked at the frozen lock until it opened, then he and his grandson loaded a dozen decoys in the boat and a five-gallon bucket with lunch inside. They attached a wire frame to the front of the old boat with screws and spent 20 minutes cutting and weaving cane switches and oak boughs into the wire to serve as a concealing blind. When they were finished the sun was filtering through the trees and a flight of ducks swept over them low, heading upstream.

"Mallards," the old man said, "that's a good sign

I reckon .... bet you we'll find a whole passel of ducks by the time we get down to the crossin'."

And so they began, the old man paddling slowly and the youngster crouched on the front seat behind the blind, watching for ducks in the pockets and backwaters.

The river itself was only 40 or 50 yards wide at the most, fairly slow with just a hint of a current. It flowed through a mixture of timbered bottomland and fields of soybeans. And it attracted waterfowl, especially when the potholes along the soybean fields were iced over.

It was only six or eight miles to the crossing where Justin's mother would meet them and the old man had paddled it many times in only a few hours. But today, they would lengthen the day with an hour or so of hunting over decoys in a flooded soybean field adjacent to the river where he had found ducks before.

Justin clutched a single-shot Marlin 12-gauge, old but well-cared for, a hammer gun with a 30-inch barrel. The year before he had used a 20-gauge single-shot but his grandfather had decided the 12-gauge would be much more suited to the long-range river jump-shooting, so he had brought it along.

"I wish I had a gun like this, Grandpa," the boy said. "Dad says maybe I'll get one next year if I learn to shoot a little better."

In a low voice, the old man responded, "There's quite a story behind that old gun ... later, I'll tell you all about it."

15

He had hardly finished speaking when a half dozen mallards took to flight from a flooded pocket 50 yards below. The old man used the situation to point out that they would have to be quiet and ready. As the paddle slurped into the water and they floated on, the boy grasped the old gun tighter. He wouldn't let the next flock get away. Fifteen minutes later they slipped quietly around the inside of a river bend and a lone drake mallard swam out away from the bank only 40 yards ahead. Justin quickly cocked the old hammer gun and slid the barrel over the top of the cane blind. He found the sight on the barrel and squeezed the trigger before the greenhead had time to react. The boy never noticed the recoil, he only knew that at last he had killed a mallard, a prize that seemed so unattainable until now. They pulled to the bank to have a midmorning cup of coffee from a thermos bottle and the old man filled his pipe.

Admiring the beautiful mallard the boy finally had to ask. "Grandpa, do you think I did wrong to shoot the duck on the water?" he asked without looking up. "I mean, everyone says it isn't sporting … but last year when we hunted over decoys I never did get a duck. I just don't think I'll ever be able to shoot that good like you and Dad and Uncle Verl."

The old man smiled as he puffed on his pipe. "I wanted to tell you about that gun there," he said. "It's a Marlin model 60, only about five or six hundred of 'em made. Oh, it ain't worth nothin' but that ol' gun means an awful lot to me. You see when your uncle was about your age he took that ol' gun down

16

to the river one day an' found three blue-winged teal sittin' on a sandbar. He crawled up over the bank and shot those teal sittin' ... killed all three with just one shot. Then he got so excited he threw the old gun down an' waded out in the river to get those ducks ... came back all wet, him and that shotgun all covered with mud. Proudest kid I ever seen."

The grandfather paused a moment to let that sink in, then we went on. "Your dad used that gun a few years later to get his first duck. I had him in a blind over on old man Anderson's slough an' he had shot up a whole pocketful of shells without pullin' a feather. Well, I went back to get somethin' an' whilst I was gone three or four gadwalls come in an' lit amongst the decoys. Your pa shot right in the middle of 'em and killed two. Got a decoy or two as well, if I 'member right."

The boy brightened at that. He could see his grandpa enjoying those memories of days past.

"Now, both your pa an' your uncle wouldn't shoot a sittin' duck now for nothin'. It ain't a sportin' thing for them, I'll grant ya. But growed men shouldn't pass such a strict view of sportsmanship on to a boy that's just beginnin'. There ain't a youngster nowhere that ain't got to learn ... an' there ain't many that ain't shot a sittin' duck when they was a youngin', so don't you let it trouble you."

The boy thought for a moment, then spoke, "Grandpa, I only got one shot, so we may not get many ducks, but if you don't mind, I think I'll try to get one flying from now on. I don't really want to shoot another duck sittin' on the water."

Again the old man smiled and he nodded his approval, "Boy, we don't have to get a big bunch of ducks to have a good hunt. I reckon we'll forget how many we brought in a whole lot sooner than we'll forget this day."

The rest of the morning Justin got a total of four shots. As expected, he missed all four. His grandfather scored a double on one flock that came back upriver, so there were three mallards in the boat when they stopped for dinner. They were only an hour or so from the old bridge, but the flooded soybean field was only a short distance downstream.

The cold that had ushered in the day was gone, the old man and his grandson shed clothing as the temperature soared toward the 40 degree mark. Some ice remained in the shallow areas of the flooded field but a pocket near the timbered fringe was open, kept that way by 30 or 40 mallards that took to flight when the two hunters appeared over the river bank.

"I think they might be back," the old man said as he watched the mallards leave. "We'll get these decoys out and get ready."

For an hour they waited, watching the bobbing decoys from just inside the fringe of willows. A few cane switches woven into the willows provided poor concealment, but it would do. The old man took great pains to point out that Justin should shoot the ducks on his side of the flock. With the wind direction the way it was, that meant the boy would have the lead ducks and his grandfather would be shooting into the trailing ducks.

The old man figured he could help some. If he timed his shot just right, he could dump that lead greenhead just as the boy shot and his grandson would think he had killed it. But unless some ducks appeared soon the plan would be wasted.

Finally, the opportunity swept in. A dozen or more mallards appeared from nowhere out over the field before them. As the hunters crouched low the old man called to the ducks and watched them turn. They passed once, and he followed them with a comeback call and the feeding chuckle. Finally it seemed they were ready. On cupped wings they slipped into the wind and came in, one old hen lead- ing and three big drakes right behind. With red legs shining in the sun, they were over the decoys, and the old man watched his grandson shoulder the old shotgun. His own gun was on the lead mallard when the boy fired and at that split second he saw the shot charge hit a trailing drake mallard and drop him dead. Jerking quickly to the back of the flock, the old man had time for only one shot and he dropped a retreating drake at the very edge of the pothole.

It was one glorious moment for the two. Justin was beside himself and in his excitement he even got water in one of his hip boots. He had dumped a fly- ing mallard in the decoys, even without the help his grandfather intended to give him.

An hour later they waited at the river crossing, the old man smoking his pipe and the boy drying his wet pant leg beside an open fire. "Boy, will Mom be surprised when she gets here," Justin said, "and I can't wait to tell Dad."

Then his face took on a troubled look.

"Grandpa," he said, "I was shooting at the other duck ... I hit the one behind. Reckon I oughta tell that?"

His grandfather had to laugh. "I've done that a time or two," he said, "never did admit it though ... reckon your Pa or Uncle Verl ever confessed to such a thing unless they had to?"

The boy's face brightened and he shook his head.

"Then danged if I would either," his grandfather replied. There was silence for a while, as the boy sat admiring the old shotgun.

"I got that old gun in 1932," his grandfather said finally. "I was about your age and the gun was about as old as I was then. My Dad traded a squirrel dog for it and promised me it would be all mine the first time I killed a goose for the table with it. Didn't take long ... I got two big Canada's off a neighbor's pond just before Thanksgiving that year ... both of 'em sittin' of course."

The old man paused and stared into space, looking back in time. "They was lots of geese came down here back then ... now they ain't hardly any. I hope someday you don't hafta tell your grandson about shootin' your first mallard without bein' able to take him duck huntin'."

That night at the old farmhouse Justin's father said it was all right for the boy to keep the old shotgun. Justin sat beside the stove, oiling it and cleaning it, wishing he could find the right words to thank his grandfather for the best gift he had ever received. But the old man needed no thanks. He was busy at the dinner table relating the day's hunt to his two sons.

Justin didn't know it then but someday his own son would kill his first duck with the old Marlin shotgun and when the time was right he'd tell him about this day.

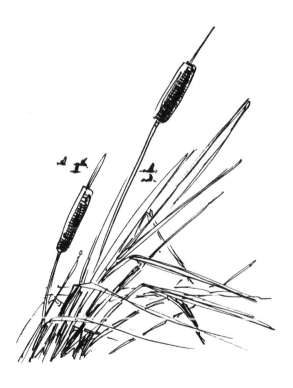

CHAPTER 3

A Christmas Puppy

He retired to the Ozarks in the mid-fifties, to raise English Setters and hunt quail and live an uncomplicated life. Well-liked in the little rural community, everyone called him by his first name by the end of the first year and you would have thought George Stephans was a native of the hills if you didn't know better.

He was admired and well accepted by everyone except one neighbor, who would always resent outsiders, especially those who came to the Ozarks with money. Seth Merritt had never had much money. He lived with his wife and three young children in a small farm house just down the road, where they scratched out a meager living with some livestock and a garden. Seth was in his mid-30's and he earned money by cutting and selling firewood, doing some trapping in the winter and some occasional work at the feed mill.

Uneducated, but proud and honest, he typified the Ozark people in that respect, but he was a hard man to get to know and winning his trust would not be easy. It was not that way with his young son, Billy. The boy was 13 and he spent as much time as he could up the road at Stephans' kennels. In a little over a year the old man had won the youngster over and he paid the boy to help with his dogs and do odd jobs around his place. In addition, he had turned him into a quail hunter. Billy had hunted for years with an old double-barreled shotgun almost too big for him to carry. But it had been good enough for squirrels and rabbits and an occasional duck on a nearby pond. Only one barrel worked and the stock was cracked, and it wasn't often that the boy got off a good shot at a covey rise. But every now and then he dropped a bob-white and one of the setters would retrieve it for him. Billy marveled at the way the dogs worked and all he talked about was the day he could own his own pup.

George Stephans didn't tell the boy about the pup that arrived a week-and-a-half before Christmas, his pick-of-the-litter to pay the stud fee the old man had demanded for the use of a big male setter. On Christmas morning, Billy would be the proud owner of a beautiful setter puppy and the old man could hardly wait. He hadn't figured on opposition to the plan, until Billy's mother got the news from Mrs. Stephans at church on Sunday morning. She showed up at his home a couple of days before Christmas, nervously fidgeting at her apron, scarcely taking her eyes from the ground.

"My husband's a proud man, Mr. Stephans," she said, "he won't have no part of takin' such a valuable dog 'les'n he earned it. He just don't want to be beholdin' to nobody."

Stephans explained that he wanted to give the puppy as a Christmas gift to the boy. The lady shook her head and stared harder at the floor. "Seth ain't goin' to allow somebody to give his boy a Christmas present like that, 'specially when we got nothin' close to that to give him ourselves"

Finally the old man was beginning to understand. And so it came to be that two days before Christmas eve he would hike up the creek to the place where Seth Merritt was cutting firewood and there would be a confrontation ... a meeting which should have taken place long ago. With a great deal of trepidation, he set forth that morning wondering what he could say to change things and if in fact what he was about to do would only make things worse.

He could hear the chain saw running up the valley and as he approached, the younger man stopped his work, setting the saw on the ground. He waited, resting himself on a fallen log, with little to say as Stephans commented about the weather. He wasn't so much unfriendly, just quiet, as he took out his pipe and began to fill it with tobacco.

"Well I see you're a busy man so I'll get right to the point," the visitor said, with his hat in his hand.

"I was hesitant to come to you with this but that old double-barrel your boy hunts with is the same one, I believe, that my dad owned when I was a boy. I remember he traded it for a rifle at the Western Auto in Ellisville way back there and I know you got it years back from old man Hankins. I've been told he lived there awhile, so it's possible he obtained it from that store after my father had traded it."

There was a puzzled look on the younger man's face but he said nothing. George Stephans went on. "I'd like more than anything to own that gun again Merritt, just to fix it up and put it over the fireplace ... something to remember my dad with you know. Always thought the world of my dad, sort of like your boy looks up to you so much.

The wood-cutter started to say something but the elder man didn't give him a chance. "Now I know it's a valuable gun, some of those old doubles will bring three hundred or so but I've got this young setter that your boy wants awful bad and the pup is easily worth a hundred dollars. I thought I'd maybe throw in a little single shot 12-gauge I've had for a time that would be a perfect Christmas present for Billy. And if that isn't enough, maybe we could ..."

Seth Merritt finally decided to interrupt. "Well, I doubt that's yore pa's gun," he said, "an' I don't know nothin' 'bout what it's worth. But shucks I reckon it could be your pa's old gun, an' if you figger it is, an' if you want it that bad I'd just give it to you."

"To tell the truth, I been thinkin' it ain't safe for the boy, an' I thought more than onc't about tradin' it for another'n. But I don't think nobody would trade nothin' for it. And for the life of me, I can't figger why a man with your money wants to fiddle with a gun that don't half work."

Stephans relaxed a bit, sensing he might pull it off after all. "Well, I guess it wouldn't be of interest to me at all if it wasn't for the memories that go with it. And I doubt I've got the money you think I've got, Merritt," he said, "and I wasted too many good years savin' what I have."

"But there's things I value more than money," he went on. "Like the memories from years back and good neighbors and friends and good dogs and the days I've got left to enjoy them in good health. You know, my grandkids are several states away but I'd give an awful lot to be able to hunt with my grandson on Christmas day. Money can't buy that. A man who can take his boy out and spend a day hunting with him and building memories, well I'll tell you Merritt, that man's a wealthy man!"

Seth Merritt lit his pipe and said nothing. You could see he was deep in thought. Finally, he spoke. "I'd shore like to see that single-barrel shotgun yore speakin' of. It sounds like what I been thinkin' on for the boy."

George Stephans could have let out a yell, but he didn't. He just pulled up a stick of firewood and the two men begin to talk ... something they had never done before. And when they had finished and the chain saw was running again, the two men had made a deal, there on that little Ozark creek in the cold grayness of winter just before Christmas.

Billy would find a nearly new, but slightly used, single-shot 12-gauge under the tree on Christmas morning and the puppy would come later, a gift from his old friend from just up the road aways.

As the older man turned to leave he was stopped short by the Ozark woodcutter. "We gen'rally hunt some on Christmas," Merritt called out, "me an' the boy that is ... reckon if you'd like to go along, Billy'd be tickled. An' I ain't never really hunted quails much ..."

"I'll be ready when you are," Stephans answered with a smile, "and I'm pleased to be invited."

Later that evening Seth told his wife of the trade. "I reckon we ought to invite him an' his wife down for Christmas dinner maybe. They got no family close, and he seems like a friendly sort ... not so much like I figured."

He kicked off his boots, leaned back in an old rocking chair, and listened to his kids at play in a nearby room. "Honey, that Mr. Stephans made me think about some things ..." he said as he took out his pipe. "An I reckon he's a pretty smart man," he said to his wife, "but it confounds me how a man that smart could know so little about shotguns – and he shore enough don't know beans about shotguns!'

CHAPTER 4

The Last Covey

George Stephans moved to the Ozarks and bought an old worn out farm which bordered the river. It was an old homestead where he could build a home and some kennels and hunt quail in the fall, a place with peace and solitude … the last place on the gravel road but for one.

The road ended at the home of Seth Merritt, a backwoodsman who worked at many things to support a family of three youngsters. Born and raised on that very ground, Merritt cut wood, trapped in the winter and occasionally took jobs in town to make ends meet. He was young and hard-working and proud and didn't much care for city folks or silk-drawered folks who seemed to have things easy. He was a hard man to talk to and even harder to get to know. But he was an honest man, and proud, and folks all said in time he'd be a good neighbor. In time he was. As the years passed George Stephans would come to be like family.

Stephans was an educated man who came from the city and wasn't well versed in the ways of the hill people. Slowly but surely he learned. But he made one friend in a hurry and that was Billy Merritt, Seth's son. The boy had originally asked if he could hunt rabbits on Stephans' land with his beagles and the neighbor could scarcely say no. After all, it was land the boy had grown up on and he would be of no threat to the quail which the old man wanted to nurture and increase.

The big black and white setter caught the youngsters eye right from the start and in the fall he watched in awe as the setter roamed before his owner, finding, setting and holding the first coveys the young boy had hunted. In time, Billy was leaving his beagles at home and hunting bobwhites, occasionally getting off a shot with his old double-barrel, finding birds harder to bag than the rabbits.

Billy understood why he couldn't shoot rabbits while the setters were along. And he understood why the big black and white male couldn't hunt as long as the other dogs. The two of them weren't far from the same age and maybe that's why the boy favored the old setter. On many occasions the dog would follow the boy home and sleep on the porch beside the Merritt's beagles.

Soon the boy and the old man were inseparable. At the age of 14, Billy Merritt was doing chores around the Stephans' place and watching after the dogs when George and his wife had to return to the city. Eventually, he got his own setter puppy, but still, the boy remained fond of the big old black and white male setter which was just about getting to old to hunt.

As he grew older and fatter, the old dog had a harder time in the field and Stephans told the boy it was best not to let him hunt much. "Only for an hour or so every few days," he advised over the boy's objections. "You have to remember that he's very old and the younger dogs are good hunters as well."

A month or so after Christmas, George Stephans had business to take care of in the city. He left the boy in charge of feeding and watering the setters. On a crisp Sunday afternoon, Billy went to the kennels and turned out only one dog ... the old black and white male who was his special companion. The old overweight setter wanted to hunt and the boy didn't see what harm it would do to spend an hour or so looking for a covey of quail.

With his new Christmas shotgun across his arm, the boy followed and the old dog ran as if he were young again, finding and holding a covey where the old homeplace had been, then another on top of the ridge where the rock fence came to a corner at the edge of the woods. The dog retrieved a bird for the boy and paused, with heaving sides, to say with wagging tail, "Nice going kid, you finally got one!"

Billy took the downed bird and then watched the big setter disappear from sight across the creek. He never saw him again! As darkness fell that evening the boy was still roaming the fields and woodlands, tearfully calling the old dog. The next morning Seth Merritt found the lifeless body of the big black and white setter behind the pond where he had drawn his last breath.

Stephans returned a day or so later and he quickly learned of the dog's death. Seth Merritt came to his door with hat in hand and they drank coffee at the kitchen table as they talked.

"I thought on givin' the boy a good lickin' for what he done," the younger man said. "But I couldn't bring myself to do it the way he was grievin' so … thought maybe his punishment would best be left to you."

Together they found the boy on his front porch, his shoulders slumped and head hung low. The tears began to flow as the older man sat down beside him.

"Billy, I guess you know you were wrong to hunt ol' Buck against my wishes, and that's why you're feeling so bad. But I was just as wrong. I owed that old bird dog more than a good kennel to spend his last days in. He didn't want that. He wanted to roam the fields 'til the very last and feel the wind in his face and home in on that smell of the quail. He wanted to see the covey rise and hear the shotgun blast and find downed birds to retrieve. And that's what he should have had ... to the very end. Thanks to you, that's the way he spent his last days, his last hours. I hope that I can be as lucky!"

With tears dripping from his face the boy didn't look up, so Stephans continued. "Now, I'm not saying it was right to not follow my instructions when you are working for me, but in this case, maybe your heart was right. Old Buck went roaming those fields with you 'cause he wanted to hunt and his old legs quit on him when he was doing what he loved the most. Why, he didn't know no pain or suffering, he just left this world in the midst of his glory. And that's a sight better than spending his last days wasting away in a kennel."

"You know that pup of yours I gave you just after Christmas is a grandson of old Buck ... I figure he'll grow up to look a whole lot like him. You and I can teach him all about bird hunting and by next fall you ought to be able to shoot a few birds over that pup."

By spring Billy Merritt was a happy youngster once again. George Stephans and his wife came for Easter dinner at Seth's insistence and that afternoon the three of them took a brace of beagles to run some rabbits behind the barn, just to listen to the chase.

That evening they sat together on the screened porch listening to the spring peepers and watching the sun set later than it had in several months. Spring was coming on fast. Seth Merritt was quiet as he lit his pipe and allowed as how he was looking forward to taking the older man up Brushy Creek to grab "yeller suckers" in early May.

Then he quietly went outside and returned with a beagle pup that couldn't have been much more than seven or eight weeks of age. He placed the pup into the arms of the surprised visitor.

"He's gonna be one fine rabbit dog," Seth said, thrusting his hands deep into the pockets of his overalls. "Me an' the boy thought maybe you might like to have 'im." As the puppy licked his hand, George Stephans thought at first of graciously declining but he did not. Suddenly he was aware that this was a special gift ... but more than a gift. It was an offer of acceptance, his chance to become one of the hill people … an outsider no more.

"You know, Seth, I have always wanted a beagle," he said. "Do you think you and Billy could help me train him?"

The younger man relaxed and a grin spread across his face. "Ain't no job to that," he said. "A good beagle comes on it a lot easier than one of them hard-headed bird-dogs. Why, it wouldn't surprise me if we couldn't get that little feller to trail birds and rabbits both … maybe even point 'em …"

George Stephans smiled a little as he looked away, his countenance hidden by the dusk. And the beagle puppy climbed up on his chest and licked his face.

CHAPTER 5

The Henry Hayes
Catfish

It was mid-March and the old man sat on the pool hall bench that morning as he had every day since he turned sixty-five in December. Everyone knew he had given up on life. He said he was just too old. Too old to run the river as he had since who could remember when. Too old to guide float fishermen, too old to hunt and too old to fish.

But Old Gabe's son had an idea, a last ditch effort to get the old-timer out of his doldrums and back into the life he had known since childhood. Everyone on the front bench of the pool room that Saturday morning knew all about it but Old Gabe.

The conversation got around to a big church dinner in mid-April. Tom Wyler said they were bussing in a group of foster children and underprivileged kids from the area. Gabe's son, Matt, said the county game warden had told him it'd be all right to donate 50 pounds of catfish to the church for a dinner for those youngsters but he just had too blamed much to do. Old Gabe just watched the pool game in progress, saying nothing.

"Tom, you or Les oughta set some trotlines in the Piney an' ketch some big ol' flatheads for those kids," Matt said.

Tom just shook his head. "Ain't gonna ketch no catfish this early. Why the river is still like ice. Just been too cold this winter. It'll be mid-April before you can do any good at all.

Gabe couldn't let that pass. "Baloney," he said. "Never seen the day I couldn't ketch flathead outta the Piney in late March."

Tom couldn't suppress a grin, but he used it

wisely as he shook his head. "You set a fair trotline in your time Gabe, but you couldn't ketch no hunnerd poun's a flathead if you had half a April to do it with, cold as that water is."

Les and Amil and Virgil all nodded agreement as a spark flickered in the old man's eyes.

"I dunno," Matt said, "Pa caught three one night in the catfish rock hole, weighed dang near a hunnerd pounds. One was 42 pounds as I recollec' an' that was in March."

"Well, I'd bet good money they ain't nobody gonna ketch no hunnerd pounds a' catfish 'fore the second Sunday in April," Les said, "I don't care if he goes ever' night."

Ol' Gabe was no longer watching the pool game. He stood up an cut himself a chew of tobacco and everyone could see a look in his face they hadn't seen in a spell. "I'll bet ever'body in this joint ten bucks I kin ketch a hunnerd an' fifty pounds a catfish before the middle Sunday of April, this year er next."

Matt rolled his eyes to the ceiling. "Pa couldn't keep it to a simple hundred pounds," he thought to himself.

That afternoon marked the first afternoon since December that Old Gabe was absent from the pool room. He was home sharpening hooks and figuring how he'd spend the sixty dollars his old friends in the pool hall would soon owe him.

He started out pretty good. Matt helped him seine a few hundred sunfish and goldfish out of some farm ponds on the widow Frank's place and they kept them in some big chicken-wire live boxes down in the creek.

Gabe caught a 16-pound flathead out of the Ginseng eddy and three more from six pounds to ten pounds out of the McKinney hole before the last weekend of March. But there was a frost just after that and a full moon to make matters worse.

By the first of April, Gabe had only 62 pounds of catfish. Matt and the boys at the pool hall were getting worried, but their hopes rose when an evening spring shower colored the water and helped warm it enough to produce a 24-pound and a 12-pound flathead. Finally, there was one more week left and Old Gabe's lines were set in his favorite hole on the Big Piney, a place known as the Henry Hayes eddy.

He needed just a couple of nights of stormy weather to get that 150 pounds. It was clear on Wednesday night but three small flathead brought the total to 123 pounds of catfish. It was plenty for the church dinner but not near enough for Old Gabe's pride. He had bet on 150 pounds of catfish and everyone knew he wouldn't be able to show his face in the pool room if he lost.

On Thursday the clouds moved in and it turned cool. Before the front, the lines were empty on Friday morning. Everyone knew the bet was lost. Everyone but Old Gabe.

The warming on Friday and the thickening of the clouds told him that there was a chance. His lines were set deep alongside the big rocks where the water was dark and quiet. He baited them early and the storm brought an early darkness.

Matt couldn't help but worry, but he knew his

dad, a veteran of countless stormy nights on the river, would find shelter in the yawning mouth of the Henry Hayes cave. He had been there many times with his dad when storms came. It was safe and dry and warm. But still, Gabe wasn't a young man any more.

The wind was strong, the lightning and thunder violent and awesome. And the rain was heavy. By midnight it settled down to a hard, steady downpour.

The sun broke through just after dawn, but the damage was done. Matt and Old Gabe's friends gathered at the pool hall early on Saturday morning knowing the river was at flood stage, knowing it was sure to have taken the trotlines with it.

There was no way to disguise the gloom with cheery words. Matt's plan had failed, now he was only concerned about his dad, hoping he had left the river in time.

"In another hour, we'll go look for him," Tom said, with anxiety in his voice.

"Ain't necessary," someone said as he entered, the screen door slamming behind him. "Ol' Gabe wants you all down to the newspaper office. They're takin' pitchers. He caught himself a 48-pound flathead last night."

Needless to say, there was a crowd at the pool hall that afternoon as Old Gabe told everyone again and again how he went before midnight to take up his lines and save them from the rising river. Over and over he told of the line surging in his hands, the tremendous struggle and the landing of the giant flathead catfish, his biggest ever. But Gabe didn't take the credit and he said he'd take no money on the bet.

"It was the Lords doin's," he said, "feeding the multitudes again with a miracle."

The church dinner was well publicized and a happy group of kids stuffed themselves with catfish steaks. It seemed as if there was indeed a multitude! The whole community was there and, of course, so was Gabe, enjoying the congratulations and retelling his story.

But he left early. Only his son Matt knew why. Old Gabe had confided in him that he had heard a gobbler on the ridge above the Henry Hayes eddy a few days before. He didn't want word of it to get out. It had been twenty years since he had heard a wild gobbler and spring turkey hunting was new in the Ozarks.

"Boy," he said to his son with the old spirit Matt had always known, "If I aim to get that ol' gobbler I got to make me a call and do some practicin' ... an' I need to figger out where he's roostin' and where he's doin' his struttin'. I ain't gettin' any younger you know!"

Matt smiled as the old man headed for his pickup at a brisk walk. "Maybe you ain't pa," he said to himself, "but lately it sure seems like it."

CHAPTER 6

The Early Buck

The old-timer knew he was in trouble but danged if he'd let it show. He just sat there on the porch, rocking easily and enjoying the autumn evening.

As the dust settled the young conservation agent stepped out of his pickup and walked toward the run-down little cabin overlooking the creek. The big hound lying beside his master paid little attention to the visitor, he was no stranger to the home of this old backwoodsman.

"Evening, Mr. Game Warden," the old man said motioning to another homemade rocking chair, "set a spell an' tell me 'bout them no good vi'laters you been a chasin'."

The agent seated himself, a grin playing at the corners of his mouth, but he said nothing.

"How's yore ma an' pa been," the old man went on, "they got over the heartache of seein' their boy go to game wardenin'?"

The young man looked toward the sky and shook his head, then proceeded to remove a paper from his pocket. "Where is it?" he asked, "Smokehouse, same as always?"

The old man tried to look innocent. "What the heck you talkin' about?"

"The buck," the agent replied. "Where is it? In the smokehouse like he's been the week before deer season every year since I can remember?"

He handed the paper to the old-timer, but the old man refused to take it. "It's a search warrant," the young man said, withdrawing it. "Makes it legal for me to look."

"Heck," the old man seemed offended, "since

when did ya need that. You had the run o' this place since you was ..."

"Now don't start that," the young man interrupted again, "you ain't gettin' out of this. Everybody and his brother knows you killed a buck this mornin', and the season is two days away."

"Wal, I reckon I did, at that," the old man squirmed in his rocker, "but I got my deer tag, right here in my pocket, an' I mean to check him jus' like I always do, come openin' day."

The agent took his hat off and ran his fingers through the heavy head of hair. For five years since deer season had reopened in 1954, the old hunter had checked a buck on opening day. Almost everyone knew the deer he checked each year had been killed a day or so in advance. In the past no one had cared much, but the new agent could ill afford to let the old man get away with it. The whole Big Piney community was watching with critical eyes to see what would happen.

"Tell me why you can't wait 'till season opens?" the agent asked.

"You know that, well as I do," the old man replied, "come season, there'll be more fools in the woods than there is bucks. I ain't gettin' out there with them greeners from the city. I ain't riskin' my neck, fer one thing, and fer another, they'll have all the bucks holed up in a thicket by mid-day. Half of 'em don't know a buck from a billy goat, an' the other half'll be too drunk to shoot straight. Ever' year I buy my tag, an' I check my buck right, an' I don't never kill but one. If'n you 'spect to haul me to jail every year, then by golly you'll jus' hafta do it."

The agent just grinned. "Ain't nobody gonna haul you off to jail," he said, "but you're gonna have to pay a fine. Reckon the judge won't make it much in this case."

"Ain't got no money," the old man said, his gaze fixed on the horizon, his jaw set with defiance. "Druther go to jail anyways, a feller ain't safe nowhere else durin' deer season with all them city fellers pourin' in here like flies on a dead horse."

"I'll pay your fine," the young man laughed outright, "but you'll have your name in the paper for everyone to see, killing a buck out of season."

The old man's eyes lit up, "My name in the paper, huh?" he asked. "Reckon they'll tell 'bout the buck, he's a 12 pointer, big as a steer too."

Placing his hat back on his head, the agent shook his head in amazement.

"So I heard," he said. "Everybody in town has heard by now I think. They're all waitin' to see if I'll just let you get away with it. If you'd keep quiet about it, an' be careful, maybe you'd get away with it, but I'm meanin' to arrest you from now to eternity if I catch you or hear about you breakin' the law. I don't like it, but by danged I can't let you get away with nothin'. If I do, nobody'll ever respect game laws in these hills."

"They won't no how," the old man said, "there's been too many crooked game wardens in here already."

"Well I ain't one of 'em," the agent replied, "If I do things right, someday they'll change their ways, too. It'll be slow, but it'll come. There'll be no game left if they don't. It ain't like it was when you was a boy, there's too many hunters now and not enough game for everyone to take what they want, when they want. We've got to take care of our wildlife and people like you have to help, eventually. Otherwise the kids born in these hills thirty or forty years from now won't ever see a deer or a wild turkey or a smallmouth bass."

The young agent paused for a moment. He knew the old man was weighing what he said. His silence meant he understood, even if he didn't like it.

"I've got to confiscate that buck," he said, "but I know you need the meat."

He paused for a minute. It wasn't going by the book, he knew, but danged if he could see the old man lose the deer. The old timer didn't have many years left to hunt and after all he was being arrested and fined as the law required.

The young man stood torn between the letter of the law and the debt he owed to the old back-woodsman who had taught him most of what he knew about the outdoors, including the love and respect he had for wild things and wild places.

"Pa says that buck'll get stolen for sure tonight when I stop by his place." He stopped and pointed a finger at the old man. "If you find one just like him hangin' in your smokehouse opening day, you get him tagged an' get him checked legal ... would you do that much for me?"

The old man nodded, he'd do that much and more to keep his deer. They loaded the buck and the agent prepared a court summons. As he prepared to leave, the old man spoke. "Saw a big flock of mallards on the Piney last week, 20 or 30 I reckon. We're goin' duck huntin' soon as deer season ends ain't we?"

"We always do," the young man replied. "I think it'd be nice if you paddled for a change and let me do the shootin', seein' as how you're gonna be in debt to me over that fine."

The old man spat a stream of tobacco juice toward the gravel road. "Sounds fair to me," he said, "shore ain't no danger of us gettin' over our limit with you shootin'."

The young warden acted indignant. "Your memory is gettin' as poor as your shootin'," he said.

The old man stood at the edge of the road and watched the pickup disappear in a cloud of dust around the bend. He turned and walked slowly back to the porch where the hound lay half asleep.

"Hot dang, " he said to the old dog, shaking his head as he looked at the summons. "Can ya beat this ... I been arrested by my own grandson!"

As he settled himself in his rockin' chair he looked down the gravel road toward the dust cloud behind the disappearing pick-up. "By gosh, Trailer," he said, "looks like law an' order has done come to the Piney."

CHAPTER 7

The Slough

The old house came alive at 4:00 a.m. as the duck hunters arose for breakfast. The fireplace was roaring. Though it wasn't suppose to be cold on opening day, something had certainly gone wrong. Bill Nettles and his friends had gathered there on opening day for many years. Years before, as a youngster, he had hunted the nearby marshes with his father, Anson Nettles, now nearly 75. Old Anson hadn't been to the marsh in several years due to poor health, but this year, feeling better, he had returned once again and he had many stories about hunts from years past.

Young Keith Nettles was there too, looking forward to opening day and some time away from college classes, hunting where he had spent so many opening days with his dad and grandfather.

But the situation didn't look good. Because of the cold, a coating of ice had developed, and the men knew old Anson couldn't wade through it to any of the three good blinds situated some distance from the roads. Those blinds, on the upper fringes of the lake where shallow water and marsh grasses attracted the main flights of ducks, could normally be reached best via boats with push-poles, but the ice made that impossible. So the hunters would have to break the ice and wade in, carrying their gear. The old man couldn't do that, but there was a blind on the slough off the river and it could be reached easily by vehicle. The hunting wasn't as good and the blind was small, but it was the only place old Anson would be able to hunt. Keith would be asked to sacrifice and help his grandfather. Of course he would.

49

Keith wanted his dad to hunt with his friends and if there was disappointment within, he'd keep it there. He reminded himself of the days, when he was only a boy, that his grandfather had spent helping him catch catfish along the river with a cane pole and worms. And the times when his grandpa had waded through briar patches to kick out cottontails for the youngster on the outside fringe with his 20-gauge single-shot.

Yes, he would gladly hunt at the slough with his grandfather, even though the slough just hadn't been much good in recent years. They unloaded gear on the frozen farm road only a short distance from the slough well before daylight. Already there was a wind, but the fringe of willow, maple and oak around the pocket would protect them from the stiff breeze. Keith broke the ice around the edges, setting decoys along the edge of deep water. He was careful, there was a lot of water over his chest waders and mud made the going tough.

The old man packed hot thermos bottles, guns, and other gear into the small blind. It was old too. Keith remembered hunting from that blind as a small boy, when he was just too little to trek back into the marsh. In those days his grandfather always was along, while the other men went off to hunt the hard-to-get-to-spots that produced more waterfowl. Keith smiled as his numb hands hurled decoys out into the water ... now the tables were turned.

Buford, the old man's aging Labrador, was excited. He sat at the waters edge, whining as he heard the decoys hit the water and wondering if he shouldn't

50

be out there retrieving them. The young man was nearly finished when he noticed his grandfather wading carefully out away from the blind with a few Canada goose decoys.

"Grandpa, I think you're wasting your time," he said. "They don't see many geese here anymore and if there are any they'll not likely be over here away from the main lake."

"I know," the old man answered, "but it brings back memories . Twenty years ago I dropped my share of honkers over these decoys, some of 'em right here. Won't hurt nothin' to have a few set out."

Keith waded over to help, shivering as the cold wind began to pick up. He couldn't help but think it was all a waste of time. Back in the blind they loaded up and waited, shooting hours 10 minutes away. Buford sat at Keith's feet, shivering with excitement as he had 10 years before. "Grandpa, remember when …"

The young man was stopped by the rush of wings over the decoys as a flock of woodducks looked over the set. "Woodies," the old man whispered, "always seems to be woodies just before time to shoot. Those ducks know shootin' hours better'n we do."

Behind the two, the wind was rushing through the treetops, limbs waving against a lightening sky. The hunters were protected by that ring of trees, but the two dozen decoys were still bobbing and swimming enticingly.

Thirty minutes into shooting hours, a flock of green-winged teal rocketed in from the river, over the short willow fringe, and barreled into the decoys. The hunters were late and only one bird went down with four shots. That duck fell far from the decoys, but old Buford saw the splash and he was on his way back to the blind with the duck almost before the excuses had begun. Keith wondered if the old Labrador would get other chances.

As if he could read his mind, the old man spoke, "You know this wind is gonna make it tough on those fellers on the marsh. But this ol' slough is protected from the wind, so you may have a surprise comin' to you today. I figger the later it gets, the better chance of them ducks lookin' for a place outa the wind. We may be in high cotton soon!"

Keith didn't say anything. His old grandfather still had his share of optimism. But as the sun rose higher, there wasn't much to be optimistic about. The duck call around the young man's neck hadn't even been used.

Just before ten that morning, Keith Nettles dozed

off a bit, warmed by hot coffee and senses dulled by the moaning of the wind in the branches behind them.

He heard his grandfather whisper, then heard him begin to call pleadingly. Roused from a shallow sleep, the young man looked over the graying boards through the cane switches to the willow border across the slough.

There was little time to pinch himself. At least 30 mallards were wheeling into the wind in front of them, dropping on cupped wings, maneuvering to approach the decoys. There would be no pass. With red legs forward and green heads gleaming in the sun, they were settling in. A couple of hens were already on the water when the hunters rose together. Keith was right on the first drake, and he dumped him in the decoys as he heard his grandfather's double-barrel roar.

Swinging on another drake, he missed clean, but the mallard fought for altitude and the wind carried him high, right above the blind. Keith knew he'd not miss his last shot. But the two guns roared simultaneously and the drake tumbled dead only a few feet from the blind, dropping into the water at the edge of the slough. Buford was after one mallard out beyond the decoys, and another, Keith's first drake, lay dead only 30 yards away. But the old man was out of the blind in a second to retrieve the third and as he picked him up, he was saying over and over, "A double.. . got a double, son.. . first time I shot at a mallard in four years and I got a double."

"Danged if you didn't," Keith acknowledged. "I got one but just shot too fast on the others." The young man didn't mind if his grandfather claimed the last bird. There were four ducks in the blind, old Buford was a pup again, and there was a spark in his grandfather's eyes that hadn't been there for a while.

Maybe it was the wind after all. More mallards swept in low, and while calling was fun, it was apparently not necessary. There were three hens which they allowed to alight and fly on, then a half dozen mallards soon after them that left two drakes on the water. Not long afterwards a good-sized flock of widgeon added two more ducks to the bag.

The last flock, scarcely an hour after the first, must have numbered 60 or 70 birds. They came in high, circled once and dropped like leaves from a whirlwind, nearly straight down into the protected pocket.

Two drakes would make a limit so Keith waited, watching his grandfather drop the first greenhead at the edge of the decoys, then miss cleanly. Only then did he swing on a fast-moving drake heading away from the blind. His first shot was on target but the mallard, hard hit, still fought to gain altitude. The second volley folded him at 45 yards and he fell into a grassy pocket at the end of the slough.

There was a great deal of backslapping and congratulations between the old duck hunter and his grandson. It was something just short of a miracle, as Keith saw it.

With ducks still flying, he finally left the old man in the blind and went with Buford to retrieve the mallard at the end of the slough. He expected the duck to be hard to find in the grasses, but Buford ferreted out the drake, still alive, from a heavy patch cover.

Keith took the mallard from the old dog and knelt to scratch his ears with rewarding words.

They were nearly back to the blind when he heard the goose call. His grandfather began calling in a frenzied, high-pitched call. Keith quickly dropped to his knees in the high grass well behind the blind as he saw the reason for the calling.

There was a flock of mallards coming into the decoys and they were only a few seconds from setting down. Behind them, three big Canada geese were turning at treetop level, heading into the pocket just to the left of the blind where the six goose decoys had been placed before dawn.

Keith swore beneath his breath. It was the chance he'd dreamed of and he was out of the blind. Anson Nettles waited until the big geese were nearly on him. Keith saw the old double-barrel crawl over the front of the blind and the first shot dumped a Canada into the slough. The other two geese flared slightly, fighting for altitude. Keith noticed that one was unusually large. He picked him up with his gun barrel, bringing the bead to a point just in front of the beak.

At the split second he squeezed the trigger, he heard his grandfather's double-barrel roar, and the Canada tumbled as the combined shots thundered across the slough as one. Old Anson didn't even know that Keith had fired, and his grandson saw no reason to tell him.

Buford watched the big goose hit dry ground behind the slough and he launched himself into action, eager to retrieve the downed Canada.

Just before noon, grandfather and grandson sat

waiting on the levee road behind the slough. In a few minutes, someone would be by to pick them up for the lunch break. They left the decoys out just in case someone would like to return to the slough because of the wind.

Buford lay sleeping, soaking up the sun's rays and dreaming of a pork chop dropped accidentally beneath the table. Such things had often happened after a good day's hunt in years past. The old man smoked his pipe, admiring the limit of ducks and geese before them.

"You know, boy," he said, "I'm plumb ashamed I shot both of them gooses."

"Don't worry about that, Grandpa," Keith answered, "I couldn't have even got a shot where I was, and I wanted one to eat ... no one has to know I didn't shoot one of 'em."

"That one gander, he's a monster of a goose," the old man said, shaking his head. "I kilt one like him onc't. .. weighed 14 pounds. I spect that'n may be close. But I jus' hate you thinkin' your ol' grandpa is a game hog."

Keith Nettles laughed. "Grandpa, do you remember when I was about 11 or 12 and we sneaked up on Mr. Kelley's farm pond all covered with mallards in that snowstorm?"

Smiling, the old man nodded as he puffed on his pipe.

"I didn't have a gun," the young man went on, "but you let me take your old double-barrel and sneak up over the bank to get a shot. I fired both barrels at those mallards when they flushed and it knocked me back to the bottom of that pond bank. But when we looked up over the top there were two or three green-heads on the water. I was so excited I didn't even notice my bloody nose."

Anson Nettles remembered. He slapped his thigh and laughed out loud.

"Well, Grandpa," Keith went on, "you never fired a shot that day and you didn't call me a game hog. Those were our ducks and these are our geese."

They could see the pickup rumbling down the levee. Both knew there'd be some surprised hunters back at the old cabin and lots of stories to be told.

"Boy," the old man said as he worked to gain his feet, "let's just tell 'em you kilt that big old gander there. I've kilt a hunnerd of 'em like that, maybe two hunnerd. I'd like for you to claim that big one of ours."

Keith nodded, helping his grandfather to his feet.

"It's been awhile since I was anxious fer tomorrer to git here," old Anson said. "Reckon me an' you can hunt here again tomorrer?"

"Heck, yes, Grandpa," the young man replied. "You can count on it. I can't think of a place I'd rather be."

57

CHAPTER 8

Old Crip

Jed wasn't one for keeping a hound that didn't earn his feed, but he had a real loser in the old bluetick everyone called Ol' Crip. The coon hunters who met around the wood stove at Venable's store had more than a few chuckles about Jed's three-legged hound. But it mattered little to the old hunter, he'd just smile and shrug it off.

Old Crip had been a fine bluetick in her day, but she had lost a front foot in a poorly placed trap set by some greenhorn trapper. Ed McNew traded the hound to Jed for a single-barrel shotgun with a busted firing pin and at that he figured he made a real trade.

Jed was set on raising some pups with the bluetick but the hound was barren. And for awhile, the old timer took a good deal of ribbing about the trade. But he shrugged it off and after awhile the hoorahin' died down a mite. Jed even took the three-legged hound on a few hunts. She'd try to hunt a little, but usually she would wind up back beside the fire. Somebody would remark that Old Crip was about ready to call it a night and somebody else would grin and recall what a skinnin' Ed McNew got on that shotgun.

Jed took it all in good humor, as it was meant. He'd just grin and whittle off a plug of tobacco and reach down to scratch the ears of the three-legged bluetick. She'd always have a good home with him. He remembered that her real name was Battle-axe, and Jed reckoned she'd have been a real battler with that fourth leg. She was game all-right and didn't set a bad pace in spite of her handicap. But when you got right down to it, she wasn't worth much to a hunter. So after a time, Old-Battle-axe became Old Crip, even to Jed.

It was in May that Alf Mayfield lost a big walnut tree to lightning. He cut it and told Jed he could have the stump to make gun stocks out of. Jed was in need of a good block of walnut. His old 97 Winchester had a cracked stock that was liable to split out anytime. So he took an axe and set forth one spring afternoon with the three-legged blue-tick at his heels.

Mayfield was sitting on the front porch patching a minnow seine when Jed and Old Crip arrived. They talked about fishing for awhile, especially the big catfish Alf caught out of the Sweet 'Tater eddy week before last. Finally, Jed allowed as how he'd best get that block of walnut and head back home.

"I reckon you know where it's at," Alf said, "Cross the crick and in the edge of the meadow where you kilt the spike buck a year or so back."

He paused, then as an after thought added, "Say Jed, Fen Marlowe's got some free rangin' hogs back over in there an' one ol' red sow is a bad one. She's got seven or eight little pigs to mind an' the job's made her meaner'n a flock of hornets. Watch fer 'er now."

Jed just grinned, "Reckon Marlowe'd miss one of them shoats?"

Alf shook his head, somber faced, "Fen mightn't but that ol' sow would. Mind what I say an' keep yore eyes peeled."

It was the kind of day which made a man want to just lay down beside the creek, somewhere and soak up the sun … like the spring flowers popping up among the chert rocks across the open meadow. The hound lingered at the creek but Jed continued on, thinking of everything in the world but that old

60

sow. It was easy to find where the walnut stood. A hundred yards before he reached it he saw the downed branches which had been cut from the trunk. They lay across the stump, so he lay the axe down and began to sling them aside.

With a startling suddenness, the branches came alive and a half dozen frightened, squealing pigs scattered in every direction like flushed quail.

For a terror-stricken moment, Jed realized his predicament. He reached for his axe and looked for the closest tree, but it was too late to reach it. She came through the woodland edge with the velocity of a steam engine, the sod and leaf litter kicking up around her like debris off a dust devil. The sow, squealing and grunting and chomping her jaws in a mad rage, rushed to the defense of her young and charged down upon Jed with speed belying her size.

Jed was 30 yards from serious trouble. He seemed frozen, but there was no place to turn, little to do but face his attacker. He had forgotten the blue tick hound, Old Crip, but she came from nowhere, a blue-gray streak covering ground as she never had before, bearing in from the side to tear at the sow's throat.

The hog was diverted. She plowed to a stop ten yards short of Jed and turned her attention to the attacker, now with a firm grip on her left ear. Squealing in anguish the hog shook the hound free and bore in. But the hound was quick and again tore savagely at the bleeding ear.

Jed hadn't moved. He had a chance to take shelter in the branches of an oak in the woodland edge, but he couldn't leave the hound to be chewed to pieces by the enraged sow. Old Crip was unable to dodge the hog easily and she was tiring. She lost her grip on the ear and went down. The sow moved in and Jed, gripping the axe with sweating, trembling hands moved behind her.

The hound tried to regain her feet, but the sow was upon her. The bluetick found a hold on the sows nose and hung on with the tenacity of a bulldog. Still squealing with pain and rage the hog now straddled the dog. The hound could no longer evade her, but she would hold on until death.

Jed never owned a dull axe and as his dog went to the ground beneath the sow, he swung it with every ounce of strength he could muster. The blade bit deep into the neck, severing the spine cleanly. The old range hog collapsed, suddenly lifeless. Jed sunk to his knees beside the bloodied, battered hound, whose jaws were still locked on the sow's nose. The word of the battle got around the Big Piney community. Alf Mayfield told of Jed returning to his house holding the bleeding hound in his arms, about as close as he'd get to tears.

The bluetick lived, patched up by the retired doctor who lived up near Bucyrus, who said she was lucky not to lose another foreleg out of it all.

Some of the fellows were in the pool hall a week or so later playing dominoes in the back, when Jed came in to join them. It didn't take long for a crowd to gather and everybody wanted to know about the battle. When all was said, Louis Moore leaned back in his chair and scratched his head.

"Who'd a thought it," he said reflectively, "Old

Crip a tacklin' a bitin' sow and holdin' er own."

Jed looked at the floor and the quiet made it plain he had something of importance to say. He reached into his overalls and pulled out a twist of tobacco. Taking his time, he cut off a plug, looking up as he returned the knife to his pocket.

"Fellers," he said, his eyes squinted between leathery cheeks and graying brows, "I know the old hound's been somethin' of a joke fer quite a spell an' I don't hold it ag'in nobody fer callin' her Old Crip. But t'other day out there on Mayfield's back 40, I 'membered her right name was Battle-axe, when she was a pup, 'fore she lost that leg."

There was a pause and before he spoke again he shook his head slowly. "When she commenced to tangle with that sow, she earned that name, far as I'm concerned. I'd as soon nobody called my bluetick Ol' Crip anymore."

For years thereafter when the coon hunters of that little Ozarks community got together to swap stories, you could hear tales of hounds that became legend to a handful of backwoodsmen. Around the stove at Venable's store, there would be talk of Old Outlaw, and Silent Jack and Old Trooper and a black and tan hound Bill Stallcup owned called Old Smoke. And every now and then with a grin and a shake of the head, somebody would mention that potlicker Jed Worley once owned . . . an old three-legged bluetick called Battle-axe.

CHAPTER 9

A Deer Hunter's Prize

There was a new .30-06 bolt action rifle in Venable's store window. A sign underneath it said …"For the biggest buck checked here. Applicants must be previously registered. Ten dollar entry fee."

Inside, several men sat around the wood stove waiting for dusk to settle. One character, the center of attention, pulled a twist of tobacco from his overalls and declared as he cut off a chew, "Reckon I'll be huntin' with that gun in the winder next year, Venable. Got me a buck spotted with a rack so big he gets tangled up in the brush every time he shakes his head."

From behind the meat counter old man Venable replied, "Jim as long as you got your ten dollars in the kitty, I'd as soon see you win it as anybody. But I'll tell you right now there's a bunch of other fellers got their ten dollars in there with you."

"Huh," Old Jim snorted, running a rough hand over his stubble of whiskers. "Most of 'em city fellers too. Reckon they'll be shootin' at everything from billy-goats to jack-rabbits. Not one chanc't in a hundred they'll hit anythin'… let alone a buck."

Jim got up and turned his back to the stove and stuck his hands deep into his overall pockets. "Only one feller I'm worried 'bout … Ol Jason over yonder."

Everyone around the stove laughed and thirteen year old Jason McElroy turned red-faced. He'd never yet killed a buck.

"Jason," Jim pulled on his jacket preparing to leave, "I want you to tell your grandpa if'n I ketch him snoopin' roun' my stand come mornin', I'm gonna call the game warden and tell 'im ever thing I know."

Jeb McElroy, Jason's grandfather and Jim's close friend, grinned and sent a stream of tobacco juice into the spittoon in front of the stove. "Why should I mess aroun' yore stan' Jim, there ain't been a buck in that neighborhood in five year or more."

Waiting for the laughter to subside, Jim had one parting comment. "Enjoy lookin' at that rifle in the winder whilst you can you old pot-shooter, come noon tomorrer it'll be mine."

Every one knew Old Jim was taking the contest seriously. He just knew that he had been seeing the biggest buck in the area and if he could get him early, before he got into thick cover, he would win that rifle. One evening just before the store closed, a week before deer season, Jim had confided in several of the local hunters that he had never before owned a new gun of any kind.

"I figger this may be my chance," Jim said that night. "Sure ain't never gonna have the money to buy anythin' new. Thinkin' back on it, most ever gun I ever got was owned by two or three other hunters, one time or t'other. I'd like just once to hold a bran' spankin' new rifle and know it was my own and hadn't never been fired by anyone else!"

Most everyone there that night, even though most of them had their money in the pot as well, hoped Jim got his wish. There weren't many of the local hunters more respected or looked up to. Jim had lots of friends and he had earned them. Whenever there was help needed he was there and when someone called on him for a favor they were never turned down. If a family came on hard times and needed meat, Jim somehow found some venison or catfish. But most folks knew he had always been dirt poor himself. His wife had left him years before because of it and two kids had moved to the city and forgotten about him. Apparently life had been too hard for them in the Ozarks. But it wasn't because Jim had been selfish. He wasn't. He had never owned anything, most folks figured, which wasn't second-hand. And he would give a friend or neighbor about anything he had.

At the dawn of the new deer season Jim had been on his stand two hours, looking over an opening where three deer trails came together. The November cold didn't affect him much any more, he'd grown use to that. But he grew stiff easily from standing in one place too long. He was wondering why he hadn't seen anything. You could hear gunshots in the distance, and it was a perfect morning for deer to move. He was at a spot between scrapes the big buck had made and he knew the deer he wanted would travel that trail eventually, the rut would make him do that.

At mid-morning, a white-tail doe, stepped into the open. Jim didn't move, he watched the doe test a motionless wind, lower and raise her head with ears erect. A smaller doe came in behind her, passed her and left the opening. The first doe lingered a minute, then followed her. Still motionless, Jim's hands tightened on the old pump shotgun that had killed so many deer in past seasons. "Sendin' yore women-folk ahead of you, " Jim thought, "Wonder how far behind you are."

The buck was noiseless, but following just as he had expected. With huge antlers, the buck was the same one Jim had been seeing and preparing for for weeks. He circled the opening following the does. Most likely they were all on the way to the river, crossing to wilder land away from the opening day crowd of deer hunters.

The buck was alert, but not all that cautious, moving at a brisk pace. Jim's gun barrel was up and when the buck looked away he brought it down with one steady movement, the stock falling in place at his shoulder. His sights were on the buck's heart in a split second, but the deer had suddenly become aware of something. He crouched just as the gun roared and Jim knew he'd missed the heart. The twelve gauge slug hit home high and rolled the big buck like the wind blowing a leaf. But in a flash, before aim could be taken again, he was gone, away through the brush toward the river.

The blood trail was skimpy, but plain and Jim followed it. He hated to press the buck too hard, but he knew someone else would have him if he didn't stay close. It was a half mile to the river. The buck had made for it in a bee-line. A good pool of blood marked the place he had lain for a time at the river bank before crossing. Jim found a shoal and crossed too. Upstream aways from where he'd entered the water the deer had climbed a high bank, walked parallel to the stream awhile, then cut up a timbered hollow. The blood was getting harder to find now. The wound had been too high. Jim cussed himself for the poor shot, then began picking up the pieces of the trail.

Suddenly a single shot rang out at the head of the hollow. Jim groaned and abandoned the trail leading toward the shots. A whoop of joy told him someone had his buck just a ways up the hollow and he figured he knew who it was. His old friend Jeb McElroy hunted at the head of that hollow. His place bordered the National Forest just to the south and it was a favorite spot.

"Reckon I'll set him straight as whose buck that is," Jim muttered beneath his breath.

Breaking into a small clearing he approached a young hunter over a big buck. It wasn't Jeb. His heart sank as he recognized the boy, 13-year-old Jason McElroy. The youngster was shaking like a leaf, nearly beside himself with excitement.

The deer had nearly ran over him and he had put one slug through the neck. About that time Jeb McElroy walked up, and it quickly dawned on him what Jim was doing there.

"Reckon this young sprout got him a buck," Jim said.

"First one I ever kilt Jim," Jason said stroking the 12 point rack. "Ain't he a beauty."

Jeb McElroy examined the two bullet wounds, then looked up at Jim. "You wasn't after this feller was you Jim."

"Naw," Jim looked away remembering years back when he'd killed his first buck." I was stalkin' one, but he was a mite bigger'n this' n."

"Never knew you to chase a deer like a hound Jim, less you had a slug in him." Jeb McElroy became very solemn and he put a hand on his grandson's shoulder. "Jason, I think …"

But Jim interrupted, raising his voice a bit, "They's lots of things 'bout my deer huntin' you didn't know bout. I don't go spreadin' my secrets roun' the country. They's things I know 'bout deer huntin' I don't want just any young sprout knowin', else he might get to beatin' me at my own game." He looked his long-time neighbor and trapping partner directly in the eye. "An if you was to go tellin' them secrets you an' me know, I'd get powerful mad at you Jeb McElroy."

Jim looked down at the beaming face of Jason McElroy with his first buck. Pulling his knife from its sheath, he looked back at the boy's grandfather, "Now what say lets me an' you teach this greenhorn how to gut a buck," he said, "before the blow flies get it."

There wasn't much doubt that the big buck Jason brought down would win the contest and it did, hands down. Jim did in fact wind up with a pretty good one, but two others beat his and he didn't even come to the store the night they handed over the prize, a week after the season. He said he had to go coon-hunting that night, he figured coon pelts would be up a little that year.

It was two nights later that Jeb McElroy came to Jim's place just at dusk and said that there was a big meeting at Venable's store about getting the game warden replaced. Old Jim had his cap on and was in the pick-up before he could get his boots tied. This was a meeting he wouldn't miss. And there was a crowd there that evening when they pulled up. There wasn't even a good spot left to park a pick-up and lots of Jim's friends had crowded into that store so there was barely any elbow room.

The old hunter pushed his way in and was quickly shoved to the center of the store. There on the domino table lay the new .30-06 rifle.

"It was to go to the hunter who killed the biggest buck, Jim." Mr. Venable said, "And that was you – even if you did give it away."

Jim was, for once, without any words. He just looked at the rifle in disbelief.

"The boy wanted a .22 rifle he could hunt squirrels and rabbits with, Jim,"

Jeb McElroy spoke from behind him. "So a bunch of us chipped in and got him one. Don't know if you'll ever get the antlers, but that rifle is yours."

There was cheering and clapping as Jim took the rifle and looked at it as if it were made of gold. You could see he was so surprised he didn't know what to do. There wasn't any speech to be made. Finally, Jeb McElroy pushed his old friend toward the door, so no one could see his eyes beginning to moisten and a tear slide down his leathery cheek.

Everyone knew the thank-you's would come later, but they weren't necessary. A man earns his place in a backwoods community by what he is, not what he owns. Jim never owned much, but he knew the value of good friends and he had plenty of them. And that night for the first time in his long life he owned a brand new rifle.

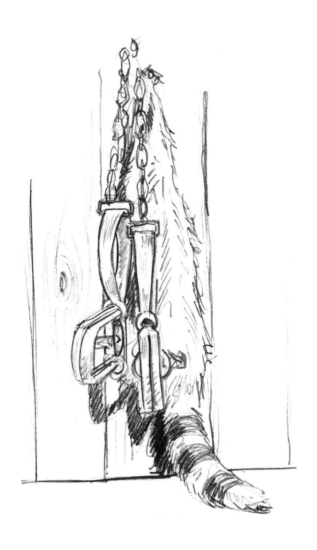

CHAPTER 10

Christmas of '49

It was December of 1949, and winter had surely arrived in the Ozarks. There was a threat of snow in the air, a deep chill riding in with low gray clouds and a north wind. The preacher braved the cold to try one more time and it wasn't something he looked forward to. He took the path leading from the cabin down to the river and found Sam Williams pulling an old wooden john-boat up on the gravel bar. He lent a hand, though he wasn't asked, and the two of them sat on a boat seat to rest as the riverman took out his pipe. "Don't want it to get froze in here in the backwaters," he said without being asked. "I aim to get back to trappin' just after Christmas."

Four mallards suddenly appeared above the tree-tops and pitched into the small slough upstream, at the head of the big white bluff which overlooked the river valley. "What a beautiful sight," the preacher marveled. "I envy you Sam, being able to make a living here in the midst of God's greatest handiwork."

"Don't envy me much Preacher Baker, cause it ain't much of a livin'," Sam allowed as he lit the filled pipe, "fur's not worth much, can't sell fish no more 'cause of the conservation bunch.. reckon I'll hafta take a town job if I can find one, or we'll lose the place sure. An' truth of the matter is, they don't seem to be none to be found."

" I know Sam, you remember I once lived a riverman's life too. But have faith in the Lord ," the preacher encouraged, "He'll get your family through this. I'm confident he won't let you down."

73

The riverman seemed annoyed by such talk. "I been a God-fearin' man all my life, Preacher. Didn't say I was about to give up. But it'll take a miracle to get us through this, and I ain't never seen none here in the hills. The wife keeps on a prayin' an' I keep a workin', but things don't change. The Lord don't seem to have no miracles for men like me."

"You talk of miracles, Sam," the preacher said, "don't forget the miracle of Christmas … the miracle of God's Son being born on earth. But the greatest miracle of all is the change in men, them becoming new and better than they were born to be. I've seen those miracles before Sam, it's just that when life gets hard at times, we don't recognize them as such. But shucks I didn't come to preach a sermon ... I just hoped you might come to our Christmas play next Sunday night … your kids are in it, an' I know they'd …"

"Hold on now Preacher Baker," the riverman interrupted, his voice rising in anger, "we've talked on this afore an' I made it clear I ain't no churchgoer. I got no time for it, tryin' to make a livin' for my family in these times. The wife and kids are there every meetin' day, an' I got no objection to that.. .but me, I got to get more done then seven days in the week allows. I figger the Lord understands that."

There was silence for awhile and the preacher sensed there was little use to go on. "He does indeed, Sam," he said as he rose to leave, "folks all know you're a good man, as good a neighbor as anyone could have, and we'd like to have you when you're ready." And then as an afterthought, he added with a laugh, "Maybe that in itself would be a little miracle Sam, having you sit through one of my sermons."

The face of the riverman lifted a little and a smile played at the edge of his rough countenance. "Preacher," he said in a low voice, "if any miracle comes my way, I promise you'll see me, sittin' there on the back row in my best overalls."

The preacher turned halfway up the path and bid farewell. "I hope you'll recognize that miracle when it comes along, Sam!"

"Don't you worry preacher," came the answer, "I reckon I'll know one when I see it." And to himself he added in a voice barely audible, "But I ain't gettin' my hopes up."

The snow started a day later and Sam was in his smokehouse preparing furs, trying to figure what he had and what they might bring, knowing it would be very little. The F.C. Taylor Company in St. Louis had sent out their price list and it was so low there would be barely enough to pay the bill at the store. Once again, there wouldn't be much Christmas.

He heard the pick-up arrive and turned to see who it was. Outside the smokehouse door he came face to face with the visitor and anger quickly rose within him as he recognized the man he considered a lifelong enemy. "What the devil you doin' here Hank?" he bristled, "Never knew you to steal during the daytime."

"Don't start that with me Sam," the visitor came back unintimidated, "I came here to talk to you man to man, not have another yellin' match. Me and you ain't kids no more Sam, we're gettin' on into our forties, an' its time to put it all behind us."

"I don't forget," Sam answered with a snarl. "I don't forget that you stole furs from my trapline and fish from my trotlines and you knocked me outa that sawmill job by lyin' about ..."

"All-right Sam, we been through that so danged many times I'm sick of it, but we'll go through it again. I'll admit I done my share of wrongs, but so did you, back then. I done no more than you. And it was yore danged hot-headedness that knocked you out'n that sawmill job, I never had a hand in it. But no matter, that was then and this is now and I've learned life is better if you admit your errors and forgive those who done you wrong and go on and try to make amends and have a better life."

"Yeah Hank, I've heared you been goin' to church regular, singin' hymns an' the like ... prob'ly reachin' in the collection plate when nobody's lookin'."

For just a moment, Hank came close to losing his composure, but he lowered his face, his shoulders sagged and he shook his head. Then he turned as if to leave, but something stopped him. For a moment, Sam felt a hint of regret at his words. As usual, he had said too darn much.

Hank didn't turn to look back, but he pushed his hands into his pockets and spoke in a solemn voice.

76

"I'm a different man than I was Sam ... an' I came to prove it to you if you'd just let me. If you'd just say maybe we could put the past behind us and try to live together in this community like human beings ... our wives an' kids get along, so can we."

Then he turned to look his long-time adversary in the eye. "I'd like to have a cup of coffee," he said, "and talk about tomorrow without relivin' yesterday. Couldn't we just once do that? I know it's a hard thing to do. It was hard comin' here even, but I done it."

In bitter defiance, Sam's eyes blazed as he remembered the past. "No sir, we sure as hell can't!" he answered, his voice heavy with anger. And there may never be a way of knowing why, but as Hank walked to his old pick-up, shoulders slumped and eyes to the ground, something quenched the anger. Something stirred a pang of regret.

The visitors hand was on the truck door when Sam Williams spoke again. "Wait ... There's fresh coffee on the cook-stove ... more'n I can drink ... we'll have some before you go!"

For two hours an argument raged, then subsided and then raged again. But finally, late that afternoon, two old enemies came to an agreement and three decades of hatred and resentment were pushed aside, slowly, grudgingly and painfully, but as surely as the seasons fade and change.

Word spread that there was a new resort going in down the river at the Slabtown crossing. The news was that Hank Slayton and Sam Williams were going

77

to build a dozen johnboats for them by spring for thirty-five dollars a boat and three dollars for sassafras paddles. And when summer came the two men, who knew more about the river than anyone else in the whole county, would guide city float-fishermen for the resort for four dollars a day and a bonus for overnight trips. Some advance money had already been paid and the two had come to an agreement that Sam would use some of it to get caught up on his land. Some said they could hardly believe the two long-time enemies had ever made such a deal. Preacher Baker said it seemed almost like a miracle!

And on that last Sunday night of 1949, when they held the Christmas play at the little country church, there was a newcomer in one of the back pews nervously re-checking to be sure his over-alls were buttoned up the front. If nothing else, Sam Williams was a man of his word.

Truth was, he didn't get much out of that play the kids put on, but he kept looking at that cross hanging above the pulpit and thinking back on Preacher Baker's words ... "The greatest miracle is the change in men ... becoming new and better than they were born to be." And Sam Williams had seen it himself. As he had told his wife that evening on their way to church ... if Hank Slayton could change that much, then it sure enough was "a honest to goodness miracle!"

CHAPTER 11

The Homeplace
Covey

Crisp but not too cold, sunshine bathing the golden hills ... a quail hunter could ask for nothing better than this.

"You know, I think these hills have grown some since I was your age," the old man told the youngster, as he rested against a fallen oak at the clearing's edge, "but this time of year, the legs feel a bit lighter."

Together they watched the young setter roam the clearing, his curiosity halting him in midstride often, as he investigated the scent of field mice and small birds at every opportunity.

"He's a beauty, ain't he, son?" the older hunter asked, recalling the hours spent in training during the past months. "I believe that pup will be an excellent dog someday."

The boy agreed. He always agreed with the old man whom he had spent so much time with over the years. He was 14, with no grandparents living and a father that worked too many hours, with little time to spend hunting or fishing. The old man had moved to the country five years before, back to the hills where he had spent his youth, after years of making it big in the city.

By the time the boy was twelve years old, he was teaching the old man how to fish the streams for sunfish and channel cat. The elder student learned well, never bothering to point out that as a youth he had fished those same streams. In return, he taught his young friend all about handling setters and together they waited each year for the coming of fall and quail season.

The new pup was nearly a year old. "When I

first saw that pup," the old man said, relaxing with his pipe, "I knew I had to have him. Reminded me of a fine big male I once owned."

The boy listened intently, his double-barrel broken down as he had been taught. He secretly wished they could be hunting on ... there was only one quail in his game bag and the afternoon was passing.

The old quail hunter had slowed up a great deal. The youngster didn't know what was wrong; his old friend didn't say much about those frequent visits to the city to see those physicians. He only knew that a couple of years before they had covered more ground.

"Well, son," the elder hunter said finally, rising to his feet slowly, "the old home place I've been telling you about isn't far now. I just know that big covey will be there. Let's go find 'em."

Along the ridge they traveled, toward the river, laughing at the young dog when he pointed a chipmunk diving beneath a stump.

"He'll learn," said the man. "Never be upset with a young dog's false points. His day will come. He just needs to know what we're after."

They came to an old rock fence, with a clearing on the other side, and a rock chimney rising from a patch of weeds. A distant look came to the old man's face and breathing heavily, he sat on the stones staring across the valley.

"The river's right over across the hillside. The barn used to stand down there at the edge of those trees. It seems like only yesterday," he said. "We played across this field, my brothers and I. That old rock fireplace, why I remember hanging Christmas stockings from the mantle. It always seemed like the time from Thanksgiving to Christmas took forever. Here it is December first already. Christmas comes so much sooner now."

It was quiet as the old man gazed across the fields grown up in blackberry and broom sage, sumac and cedar. The pup came back to rest with them, and he rolled in the dead leaves with the exhilaration of youth. He was indeed a fine-looking young setter, nearly pure white, with one small red spot on his ear and another the size of a coffee cup on his rump. Other than that he was pure white, no freckles, no specks along his legs.

"You think we'll find a covey here?" the boy asked impatiently.

"Sure," the old man answered confidently. "There was always a covey here, long before the buildings burned. As boys, my brothers and I would whistle up bobwhites in the spring, right up on the lawn. We'd shoot them with an old .22 Stevens single-shot rifle. Never got many, but now and then ..."

There was a long quiet as he remembered. Slowly and solemnly he spoke, his mind on a small country family of the 1920's, and a carefree life that left such treasured memories. "I wish I'd never left here, son. Why is it a man finds out so late in life where real value lies and how easy happiness is to find!"

"'Why did you go?" the youth asked, as he knelt to scratch the belly of the pup.

"Money I guess," he sighed. "It seemed more important then, and the city so attractive. I spent so many years frantically clawing away after success for five days a week. Then I'd head down here in a mad dash with my dogs to spend a weekend chasing Mr. Bobwhite or trying to catch old bucketmouth from the pond!"

"I'd like to give you some advice, son," the old man said, still gazing across the fields before them, "but I won't. You wouldn't listen any more than I did. Remember this, though. Success, happiness, contentment, whatever ... it can't be caught. Don't chase it like that young pup chasing a mouse. And don't look for it across the river. It's never very far away."

As they set forth behind the enthusiastic young setter, the old man spoke again. "I don't know why old age makes a man see things so much more clearly. Maybe it's because it's easier to see things looking backwards. But these hills are the place to be, son, not a place to look back to."

Suddenly the setter pup was gone. They topped a small rise and there he stood, frozen, head low and tail high, the scent before him strong and tranquilizing. The boy shook again with excitement. "Think it's a rabbit?"

The old man smiled. How many times had he found them right here, only a short distance from the old home place? Generations of bobwhites, year after year, new individuals to replace the ones that the winter had claimed, holding their own as the years rolled by and young pups turned into memories of fine dogs as youngsters became men, and then became old hunters to guide a new generation of puppies and boys.

"No, son," he said, still smiling, "it's not a rabbit.

You'll have one chance at these birds before they head across the river. They always do."

When the covey flushed, the old man brought his gun to his shoulder and followed a fat bobwhite out of range. He didn't fire, but he heard the youngster's double barrel roar … two shots, far too close together. But the youth was beside himself with excitement. "I got two;" he hollered at the top of his voice. "I got two."

No one would ever know if he actually scored a double or downed two crossing birds with one pattern. But it mattered little. The young setter retrieved one and almost made it back with the second before he stopped to play with it. The old man scolded him halfheartedly and handed the pair of birds to the beaming young hunter.

It was quite a time for the three of them. The boy's first double as well as a picture point and retrieve by the pup. The old man knew this moment would be relived for years to come.

As they roamed the afternoon fields together, circling back toward the pick-up, the old man decided not to say anything about his upcoming trip to the city. With his health failing, he felt it best to take the older dogs back with him. They might never return to these hills, he knew.

The young setter would stay with the boy. His father had already agreed. They were ready for each other, these two youngsters, the old man told himself. The future would be theirs ... the golden fields, the memories of those great days and the old home place covey. Yes, they were ready. It was time!

CHAPTER 12

The Turkey Guides

Lucas Schmidt and Jake Edwards were partners — trapping partners, fishing partners, hunting partners. Together they fished, hunted and trapped on the front porch of Venable's store. And when it got cold, they moved inside before the old iron wood stove, helping to draw the gatherings of local backwoodsmen and an occasional passer-by.

Venable tolerated the pair and their endless yarns and recollections. They were good for business. These two old-timers were friends of his, and everyone else for that matter. Lucas was a widower who lived with his son Richard and his family. Jake was a bachelor.

They were veterans of many fall hunts, witness to the days when black bear roamed the Ozark mountains and river otter played along the Big Piney. They were mere youths in times when wild turkey flocks roosted in the bottomlands, 70 and 80 in a flock.

Together they recalled those days on Venable's front porch as the first days of April made the dwindling woodpile insignificant. For many years there had been no turkey season, and now, early in the 1960's, the gobblers were again fair game for a handful of hunters who ventured to try. In the Ozarks those numerous dry years had made turkey hunting a lost art. Jake was whittling away on a chunk of cedar when the city feller drove up to the gas tank. "Plain to see he was a city feller," he later explained, "all gussied up, an' his hair slicked down with fancy rings an' a tie an' the like. He comes right up an' reckon's this cedar I'm a whittlin' on is a turkey call or he's a ring-tailed alley cat. So I says, 'why yes, reckon I'm fixin' to call in a long-bearded tom first day of the season an' blow his fool head right off.'"

"Been a few y'ars since you killed a wild gobbler, ain't it Jake?' Richard said with a grin, shifting his pipe.

Old Jake looked at his feet and muttered, "A spell I reckon, but I wasn't about ta tell 'im that. Then Lucas here goes to blowin' an' a spoutin' 'bout all the gobblers we called in with them cedar boxes, an' this feller takes a notion he'll hunt him one, too."

Lucas objected, "Just a danged minute Jake, you's the one doin' most a the talkin', I jest agreed to go along an' do my part."

Richard, Lucas' son, who had been listening to all the chatter looked up from his grindstone and leaned on his axe. "Agreed to go along with what?" he asked suspiciously.

Jake stared off across the Big Piney valley, his hands thrust deep in his pockets. Lucas chose to answer, "Well, this feller decided to hire us for guides ..."

Richard rolled his eyes toward the heavens and Lucas hurried on before he could reply.

"... an' I was fixin' to tell 'im that we ain't hunted turkeys for quite a spell, when he up an' offered a hunnerd dollars if'n we can call one up so's he kin kill it."

"Pa," Richard broke in, "you an' Jake hunted

turkey when they was thick as warts on a hackberry. I've heard a thousand times how you scattered 'em off the roosts in the middle of the night an' waited for 'em to regroup beneath the roost at dawn. That don't work in the spring. Besides that, it ain't sportin'. You fellers can't work a call, an' you ain't got no idea where a single wild turkey roosts between Tony Hogan ford and the Gasconade river."

"'Tain't so," Jake said, hands still deep in his pockets, his eyes fixed on the ground. "If'n we had the time, I know where there's a gobbler with a beard as long as …"

Richard Schmidt wasn't listening. He grinned, wondering to himself what important matters were keeping the pair so far from Venable's front porch. He knew what was coming. His old domestic gobbler was a half-wild barnyard bully and he had threatened to dispose of him on occasion. Jake and Lucas were there to make a bid for the old tom, visions of an easy hundred dollars sending the wheel spinning. As he tuned back into the conversation, Lucas was putting forth his best effort.

"Now, you said yoreself that ol' gobbler was gonna hafta go after he up an' flogged little Richie that time he was feedin' the chickens."

"How much you fella's figure to pay?" Richard asked with a grin, thoroughly amused by now.

"Ten dollars seems fair 'nuff for a turkey I reckon," Lucas offered.

Richard turned back to his grindstone as if he

didn't hear. "Don't know where a feller'd buy a big ol' gobbler for ten dollars. I couldn't part with that ol' tom of mine for less than twenty."

Jake and Lucas were in a tough position to bargain. Richard knew what they stood to make. They gave a final offer, fifteen dollars and a young gobbler as soon as they could rustle one up. Richard thought awhile, then accepted. Lucas and Jake headed for the barnyard, but the younger Schmidt halted them.

"Paid in advance," Richard grinned. "Not that I don't trust you fellers, but they's times when you been a mite forgetful."

Jake and Lucas dug into their pockets. It was a small investment for such easy profit. The Kansas City hunter was elated at the prospects of bagging his first tom. The barnyard gobbler was a bit indignant, however. At midnight before the opening of the season, Jake and Lucas hauled him to a heavily-wooded ridge overlooking the Piney. They secured the big bird to a sassafras sapling with heavy braided nylon fishing line, and then released him from the crate. Held fast by the leg he sprawled out on the ground, wings spread, looking like anything but a majestic wild gobbler.

"Hope he gets his pride back 'fore first light," Jake said as they stumbled through the woods in the dim light of a swaying kerosene lantern. Neither of them would say it, but they were also hoping their gobbler didn't become the victim of a passing bobcat or a pack of coyotes.

The hunt itself was well rehearsed and, at daylight, the turkey guides were there with their client, anxiously waiting with his shotgun in hand and his back to an oak tree. The hapless gobbler was secured less than 40 yards behind him.

Jake situated himself a few feet to the side and began to scratch away on cedar box. Lucas sat beside the hunter, waiting to point out the gobbler. He'd have to move fast to cut the line from the turkey's leg, but the old-timers were sure everything would work as planned.

First light seeped slowly through the woodlands as the greenhorn hunter waited. Terrible thoughts began to seep in, too. Jake and Lucas began worrying about whether or not the grounded gobbler was still there. What if the bird somehow worked loose and had escaped in the night?

To their relief, the gobbler was still there, one leg stretched out behind him, and wings flopped out a little. But he had his head up and that was all that mattered. Lucas didn't wait for the morning to get real light. He had explained to the greenhorn how a gobbler could spur a hunter in it's death throes and told him just to wait where he was after he shot one. He said he'd quickly fetch the old ground-raker in. It appeared that the pair was about to make an easy hundred.

But the city hunter threw a knot in the rope. He was shaking like a leaf while Jake scratched away on the cedar box and when Lucas told him a big gobbler had snuck in behind them, he went to pieces.

He jumped to his feet and emptied both barrels at what must have been the luckiest old barnyard gobbler in all of the Ozarks. The bird went down all right. Straining against the taut line, he went down hard as two loads of No. 6 shot wiped out a two-foot section of braided nylon.

When he gained his footing, the turkey headed with determination for the depths of the Lewis and Clark National Forest, head down, kicking up leaf litter behind him.

The hunter cussed his luck, but it took Lucas only a few seconds to recover. He allowed as how the gobbler was hit bad and he and Jake would find him. They took the crestfallen client back to his car at Venable's store and made arrangements to meet him later when they had tracked down the old tom.

Shortly afterward, the old pickup was heading toward Richard Schmidt's place, both old-timers praying that the gobbler was a homing turkey, waiting that very minute at the barnyard gate. The gobbler had no homing instincts, but fate dealt the two guides another pair of aces.

Sixteen-year-old Richie Schmidt had skipped school that morning and bagged his first gobbler. It was a young tom with a five-inch beard, 15 or 16 pounds at the most. Jake said it was too small for a feller to take to the check station and Lucas reckoned it was a shame Richie wouldn't be able to skip several more days of school, since he'd already killed a gobbler.

This had an impact on the youngster. Clearly he wanted to keep hunting and his turkey was no ground-raker. But it was a gobbler, and he reluctantly decided to take the young tom to the check station. It took twenty dollars to change his mind!

By 9 a.m. Richie had headed back to the turkey woods and Jake and Lucas were headed for town to find their gullible Kansas City hunter. They had the situation in hand and it was all down-hill from there. At the check station, the hunter posed for the local newspaperman with his gobbler as the two guides who claimed to have tracked the crippled tom for two miles watched on.

That afternoon, Jake and Lucas sat on the porch at Venable's store reliving the incident with their client and a half-dozen front porch turkey hunters. They remained there, still going over the details with whoever would listen while their client went back to his motel for his checkbook.

It was the last either of them saw of him. By dusk that evening, it occurred to them he wasn't coming back, nor was he anywhere to be found in town. Jake and Lucas had been had. It was a week before either hunter made it back to the porch at Venable's store. During that time, Richard Schmidt's old gobbler got tired of scratchin' for a living in the thick of the wilderness and wandered back into the barnyard with a few feathers missing and not quite the cock-of-the-walk he had once been.

Richard, after a time, returned to Jake and Lucas their money, plus the twenty they had given to young Travis, who shot a 23 pound wild gobbler off the roost the third morning of the season.

The two guides never got their picture in the paper, but Richie Schmidt did. He and his big gobbler made better reader attraction than the city hunter and his scraggly yearling tom.

In time, Jake and Lucas forgot the whole thing. In fact, a few months later, and each spring season thereafter for many years, they could be heard telling the story of the dern fool city feller that had emptied both barrels at a tame, ground-anchored turkey and missed. Jake would laugh and shake his head while Lucas recalled how they had fooled the feller with Richie's yearling gobbler and how proud that greener was with his trophy. Then after the knee-slappin' had ended, Jake would cut another plug of tobacco and remark, "Yessir, I reckon that city dude don't know any different to this day … gullible as a spring hen, sure as sin."

CHAPTER 13

Old Smoke

Because of the falling snow, there were a lot of empty chairs around the stove in Venable's store. Old timers Bill Stallcup and Pete Barnes were there as usual, talking about the snow and remembering worse winters way back there.

Twelve year old Travis Sutterfield was there too. School had been called early because of the snow, and he waited at Venable's store for his dad to come by after work.

"Never seen such a long face," Bill said as the youngster sat down beside the old man he idolized. "Looks like yore scared t' death school may be called off fer good."

"I didn't make the basketball team," the boy sighed. "I ain't good enough. Seems like I ain't good enough at nothin' sometimes."

"Didn't know you was so set on playin' basketball," Bill said.

"If you don't play basketball, or baseball or somethin'," the youngster replied, "then you ain't very popular."

He put his head in his hands and looked at the floor. "Everything I'm good at ain't important."

The old man looked across at his comrade and winked, then he took out a twist of tobacco and slowly cut himself off a plug.

"Well sir, I'm a gonna tell ya," he said as he replaced his pocket knife, "I had me a dog onc't named Ol' Rounder." He glanced at the boy, "Never hear'd tell of him did ya."

The youngster shook his head. "Wal, he was a fine one," the old man went on. "Big ol' black 'n tan

97

... could tree more coons in one night than I could tell about. Why he was big an' strong, could run all night. Many's the coon hunter what offered me a hunnerd dollars fer 'im."

The old timer paused a minute, looking into space as he went back to days long past. "Then I had me a young hound I couldn't a sold fer a five dollar bill."

"He'd hunt with ol' Rounder, but he couldn't hardly keep up with 'im, just foller 'long. Never hit a trail on his own, never had much of a voice."

The boy was all ears, this was a story he hadn't heard before.

"Well your grandpa had a good dog too," Bill continued, "a fine hunter he called Ol' Jack. Me an' yore grandpa hunted a spell with them three dogs one winter way back yonder. Some of the other fellers went along ever now 'n then, an' they'd laugh at that young dog tryin' to keep up with Ol' Rounder an Ol' Jack."

"Well sir, one night we wuz huntin' coons in the Horseshoe Bend bottoms when the dogs tree'd way up yonder by the Mineral Springs road, so fer away you could barely hear 'em. Fer some reason, the young one had stayed right with me that night ... wouldn't leave my side. The feller's were givin' me a hoorahin' 'bout that dog and I wanted to get him up where the others had treed, so's he'd get the notion of what he was s'pose to do. So while everybody else took to the long bendin' ridge, I figgered I'd take a short cut right up the river."

Ol' Bill shook his head, gesturing with his hands,

"I reckon you know that little bluff right over the tow-head eddy."

The youngster nodded and Bill went on. "Well I was a walkin' along that steep hill above the bluff with that young hound follerin' along behind, when some loose rocks give way and I went to bouncin' down that hillside."

The boy's eyes were big and he was carried away with the excitement of the story. Bill sent a stream of tobacco juice into the ash bucket beside the stove and went on.

"Well I saved myself by grabbin' a little bush right by the edge of the bluff. But jus' when I thought I was gonna get outa that jam, the bush pulled loose an' down that bluff I went, right into the Towhead Eddy."

"Reckon I hit my head on the way down, cause I just nearly went out. Next thing I 'member, that blue-tick was right in there with me, pullin' me out by the shirt."

"Dang she was cold," the old man shook his head. By now, even Pete was interested in the story, and Venable had paused to listen. "I knowed right off my leg was busted, an' I didn't have a dry match to build a fire. Didn't even have my light. I jus' laid back an' the pain was so bad I passed clean out."

"Next thing I know's I'm at yore grandpa's house, an' the doctor is workin' on me. Well, I come to find out the young dog not only pulled me out of the river, he commenced to bawlin' like he's treed a passel of coons. It brought the rest of the fellers to where I was stretched out on the bank, that hound layin' beside me tryin' to keep me warm. Most of 'em said they'd never heard such a voice as that hound come up with that night."

"Well, you never hear'd me talk much 'bout Ol' Rounder, but you've hear'd lots about that young dog, it was Ol' Smoke hisself."

The youngster's eyes lit up. Ol' Smoke was something of a legend in the Big Piney area.

"I never told nobody this," Old Bill leaned back in his chair, "but I've had lots a hounds bigger an' faster than Ol' Smoke, an better hunters too. But Ol' Smoke had character, son, an' that's more important than anythin' else. Same way with folks. It don't do no good just to be a good ball player.. don't mean much to be popular if you ain't got character. Won't be long 'til nobody'll member who played ball best," the old man said. "Some of them fellers that's popular now won't never 'mount to a thing when they're growed up. They'll go to workin' an' raisin kids an' worryin' about gettin' the bills paid. But if a feller's got character, he's somebody. And a feller who has character is gonna go someplace and do big things. Sooner or later you find out they's somethin' you can do better'n anybody else, an' you got to work hard at that. If you got the right character, like Ol' Smoke had, then you'll make 'er big, son; someday when it's really important ... maybe be a doctor or a policeman or a governor."

"Old Bill paused for a moment and thought about that. "Maybe not a governor, I don't reckon. Ain't got to have much character to be a politician, but you get the hang of what I'm tellin' you, boy!"

The youngster left in higher spirits when his dad stopped by that evening, and when he was gone Pete Barnes looked at his friend with skepticism.

"I never knowed a thing about all that, Bill," he said, grinning. "You a breakin' yore leg an' all. All of it actual truth I s'pose?"

Bill tried to look nonchalant. "That's not just exactly the way it happened," he said, in a serious tone, sending another stream of tobacco juice toward the ash bucket. "Truth of the matter, Ol' Smoke built a fire an' set my leg hisself."

CHAPTER 14

A Christmas Lesson

It wasn't much snow, three inches at the most, but it produced the first white Christmas the twelve-year-old Travis Sutterfield had ever seen. There'd never be another Christmas like it for the youngster. He had received his first gun. It was an over-and-under 20 gauge/.22 rifle combination, purchased second hand from a neighbor for 20 hard-earned dollars. In the early 1950's, twenty dollars was a lot of money, but in the Big Piney River country of southern Missouri, it was imperative that a youngster growing up know how to use a gun safely and efficiently.

"You know," Ol' Bill said as he lit his pipe, "I 'member when you got your first gun." He was talking to the elder Sutterfield, now in his thirties but still a youngster to Ol' Bill, who had spent more than 60 years on the Big Piney. Bill lived downriver a mile or so, at the mouth of Horn Creek. On Christmas morning, he left early to paddle an old johnboat upriver to the Sutterfield home overlooking the Ginseng eddy. Later in the day there would be a Christmas dinner with all the Sutterfield clan gathering, but Bill was always the first one there and he was always welcome.

"I might have been younger in years when I got my first gun," Rob Sutterfield said as they rocked before the old stove which radiated warmth on that gray Christmas morning.

Sensing he left something unsaid, Ol' Bill took up for the youth. "Why that boy Travis can shoot with the best of 'em."

"That ain't what I'm gettin' at," Rob replied,

knocking ashes from his pipe in the ash bucket by the stove. "You an' pa got his head too full of huntin' stories. All the boy knows is shootin'. He ain't really learned to hunt."

The old riverman pondered that, peering out at the few small flakes of spitting snow warning of the potential of the low clouds.

Rob refilled his pipe and went on. "Times are changin'. A hunter isn't measured nowadays by his shooting eye and a set of antlers. Now Travis knows how to shoot ... you an' pa taught him that all right. Trouble is he ain't learned when. Seems a mite too trigger happy to me. Everything is a target."

The old man said nothing, solemnly rocking before the fire. He had never considered that point.

When Christmas dinner was over in late afternoon, Travis had his new gun ready. Bill had promised they'd hunt rabbits together. It was still cold and gray, a half-inch of new snow had accumulated from intermittent snowfall. Bill allowed there'd be more snow that night as he and the boy set out for the river bottom fields.

The beagles, Amos and Andy, got distracted and were running a noisy circle on the timbered ridge above them. Bill left the youngster at the edge of a tangle of blackberry thickets, and headed up into the timber to retrieve the beagles.

Travis sat patiently, fondling the new gun and shouldering it occasionally, imagining a big wild goose folding before him at the touch of the trigger.

Ol' Bill hadn't been gone long when a shadow drifted down the draw across the field and a beautiful red fox glided into the clearing and headed toward the river.

Travis's pulse quickened. He flipped the selector button to the rifle barrel and watched the fox stop at the edge of the clearing he had just crossed. He fired quickly and the fox, at 40 yards or better, dropped in its tracks.

The boy was elated. He let out a yell and ran to his fallen quarry, anxious to tell Bill what a long shot he had made. When he knelt in the snow beside one of the most beautiful animals he had ever seen, there was a sudden tinge of regret. He fought that feeling off as he saw Bill crossing the field toward him.

"You should have seen it, Bill ," he began. "I was way over there ..."

"That's a strange lookin' cottontail," Bill interrupted, shaking his head. "Reckon he'll be good eatin'?"

Travis felt a stab of guilt. "I thought I'd skin him out an' maybe sell the hide," he said, looking away from the old man's somber gaze.

Bill produced a sharp knife and knelt to begin the skinning. With his experience as a trapper in years gone by, it wouldn't take long.

"Fur prices ain't much," he said. "Sure seems a shame to end the life of a wild animal like this just for a few dollars."

Travis could sense an air of disapproval. "Just

a fox," he said, "guess he won't get no more of ol' man Fleenor's chickens."

"Fleenor don't take much care of those chickens." Bill talked as he carefully worked on the thick red pelt. "Every time his dog catches one he blames it on a fox. If a feller don't keep up his stock, he should expect to lose a few. This ol' fox had folks here a long time before Fleenor came. Seems like maybe he ought to have a right to a chicken every now an' then."

The boy knew now his act hadn't found favor with Ol' Bill . "What about the rabbits these foxes eat. I reckon I saved a few of them."

"Fer what?" Bill looked up for a moment. "Fer us? Are we any different from this ol' fox? He hunts rabbits to eat, so do we. He eats a passel of them mice too."

The boy was quiet, his head hung low. He couldn't defend the hasty shot.

Working the pelt loose, Bill went on. "This fox here, an his kind, don't kill just fer the sake of killin'. The Good Lord put him here to keep up with the rabbits and mice. He ain't no better or worse than all the other living things. The fox don't worry hisself with figgerin' out what should be here an' what shouldn't, he just takes what he needs an' nothin' more."

Travis had nothing more to say. Kneeling in the snow, he watched the old man remove the pelt fully aware that he had taken a life for no good reason.

"Naw, I wouldn't sell this here pelt boy," the old

man sensed his shame, and decided he had been harsh enough. "I'd keep it an' remember what a fine hunter this ol' fox was. An' always try to be that kind of hunter yourself."

They walked back toward the homeplace as evening slipped quickly toward nightfall. It seemed to be growing colder and fine snow stung their cheeks as they faced the wind.

There'd be more Christmas hunts as the youngster grew older. But none would be worth more. For years, the tanned hide of the red fox would hang on the wall above his bed. Maybe because of it, he'd be a more responsible hunter.

Asked about the aging pelt in years to come he'd just say it was a Christmas gift ... from an Ozark wise man!

107

CHAPTER 15

Outlaw

I don't remember when the old hound wasn't around, he was that old. Jess called him Outlaw ... raised him from a pup. In his day he was a big powerful trailing hound with a voice they talked about all across the county.

I remember those nights in the Big Piney river valley when old Outlaw struck a hot trail and all the talk around the campfire would stop. In the silence, the lonesome bawl of the legendary hound floated over the hills, distinct from the baying of the other dogs, so powerful and strong it sent a shiver down my backbone.

Maybe you wouldn't call it music, but Jess and the other men knew it as such. All I know is, the voice of old Outlaw was different than any fox along the river had ever heard before. I remember that year as I grew older and winter came on, how the aging hound became stricken with disease. He didn't eat much and he lay around most of the time growing thinner and lazier by the day. He was beginning to lose his teeth when Jess brought Outlaw to the vet.

"How old is this hound, Jess?" the veterinarian asked, shaking his head as he looked him over.

"Right at thirteen years, I reckon," the old woodsman answered.

With sympathetic eyes, the doctor looked into the weathered face of the hunter. He knew Jess and he knew his advice wouldn't be easy to swallow.

"He's old and sick, Jess," the vet told him. "Maybe if he was younger I could help some, but at his age there's nothing I can do. He'll just go downhill and sooner or later you'll need to put him

to sleep to keep him from suffering."

Jess took it hard but he never let it show. The ring of old-timers who looked forward to those winter fox hunts with such jubilance now prepared for a November hunt with sadness. Jess had announced it would be old Outlaw's last chase. It was cold that night and some said they could feel snow in the air. Fallen leaves lay along the old logging road that led down to the river and they crackled beneath the shuffling feet of the hunters. It was just like always before, with most of the men joking about someone else's dog or telling some wild story about the past deer season. Only Jess was quiet.

Everyone acted like nothing was different, but there was a strained atmosphere that night. Grandpa had instructed me to not ask any questions and that was a tough job for a 13-year-old boy. But I tagged along quietly behind, heart saddened and feet heavy.

Old Outlaw walked beside Jess for a long while, unlike the times in years before when he was the first hound on the trail. The other dogs had headed for the river upon being released. Jess's other hound, a young pup, kept returning to the group as if urging old Outlaw to joint him.

But the big hound stayed by the side of his life-long friend and master, his muzzle never far from the old woodsman's hand.

No one seemed to notice when he left us, but as we grouped around the fire on the river's edge, I noticed that Outlaw was gone. The other hounds had a chase going back to the south and most everyone assumed he had joined them. But as the first chase faded farther away, there came a long deep bawl from the low ridge to the east which paralleled the river. There was no mistaking that voice.

Suddenly the talking stopped and most of the men rose to listen one last time to those clear, long, drawn-out notes. I stood too, with those chills playing up and down my spine again like always before. Jess's young hound joined Outlaw for awhile, but as the chase left us and crossed the river downstream, the young dog returned to the fire, apparently somehow aware that this trail belonged to Outlaw alone.

Across the river, the pursuit turned upstream again and Outlaw's voice became strong as he moved near us. I wondered how that voice could remain so clear and deep and strong while the old hound became weak and frail with age. Most of the men couldn't believe that those aging legs could carry the big hound as far as the chase had led him, but the voice never wavered and Outlaw forged on, hot on the trail of another fox. Jess moved out away from the fire and stood alone, his hands thrust down into the pockets of his overalls, his mind way up on that ridge with his dog. I was glad that the darkness prevented everyone from seeing his face … and mine.

But now the chase turned away, high into the hills across the Big Piney, westward into the vast timbered expanses of the National Forest. We listened in stillness as the old hound's deep, bellowing voice became harder and harder to hear, eventually silenced by the distance.

Outlaw never returned that night. For several days Jess went back to that spot on the river to call and wait for his dog but I don't think he expected to see him again. Outlaw must have sensed it would be his last chase. Oh, I knew that dogs couldn't think or reason but I liked to imagine he knew it was better that way, better especially for the old man who loved him so much he could have never made that last trip to the vet.

Some of the men figured he had caught up with the big old red wolf that they said roamed those river hills and some said maybe he trailed a mountain lion to his doom. But I don't know, I wonder if he didn't just keep running until those tired old legs would carry him no farther.

Age may have stopped those old legs and stilled his strong heart, but nothing could have stilled his voice. I can hear it even today. On a cold, clear November night it echoes across the valleys of my memory and I can see old Jess standing there in the edge of the firelight saying good-bye to his old friend.

Occasionally, hunters along the lower Piney claim they hear an extra voice in with their hounds on a cold winter night ... a voice deep and clear, which seems to fade away into the timbered hills to the west. And one old trapper who travels the river in the midst of the winter swears that on a still night, if you stand quiet and listen hard, you can hear the far away baying of a hound ... a hound with a voice of pure gold, beginning and ending deep in the wilderness across the Big Piney where the spirits of old fox hunters are listening still.

CHAPTER 16

Wally's Buck

I stopped by Wally's place late in the winter. His big buck was back from the taxidermist. It was only the second one my friend had killed. But what a rack! It was a broad-beamed, nine-pointer anyone would have been proud of.

"Who would have thought when we were kids playing in the creek on my grandfather's farm that the place would be mine someday," Wally said ... "and that it would have bucks like that."

Sitting down in his favorite chair, Wally lit his pipe. "I've never told anyone the full story about that buck, but I'm gonna tell you 'cause I can't stand to to keep it to myself."

So with the snow falling and the coffee cups full, the two of us went back to mid-November and the farm 200 miles away where we had spent a big part of our boyhood together.

Wally hadn't seen the back reaches of the farm since 1969, but things hadn't changed much. Well in some ways they had and in other ways they hadn't. There were still sunfish in the swimming hole on the creek, though it had filled in a lot. When we were boys, we caught those sunfish on cane poles. Back then, they were whoppers, prized catches for a pair of youngsters.

Wally said he marveled at the size of the sycamores along the creek. He said there was a screech owl staring from a hole in a big white limb where the old tractor road crossed and he remembered listening to the wailing cries of screech owls as a boy, snuggled deep in the soft feather bed of his grandparents' upstairs bedroom.

Along the farm's back boundary lay the crumbling remains of the old rail fence which marked the farm's boundary and he was drawn to that spot like a magnet. Just on the other side was the remains of an old cabin where Uncle Joe had lived. Old Joe wasn't anyone's uncle, but we had always called him that. We spent many hours at his old cabin listening to hunting stories. We were in college when Uncle Joe passed away. He was buried beside his little cabin, but neither of us could make it back for the funeral.

Wally felt bad about that. As he visited the old place just before deer season he found the old man's grave and cut some of the weeds around the headstone. Then he drank from the spring near the collapsed cabin and stood for awhile on the porch, remembering. Most of the porch remained upright, supported by two big cedar posts.

Uncle Joe used to stand up, stretch and strike a match on those cedar uprights, light a small scrunched-up cigarette he had rolled himself and then say, "Now then boys, where wuz I." We'd help him remember and he'd continue with the story.

Sitting there in Wally's den, I smiled at those pleasant memories. But Wally was stone-cold serious, as he told me more about the big buck.

"You were off in school when I killed that fork-horn buck in '65. I was 17 and it was my first deer hunt," Wally said, still sober-faced, with a far away look in his eye.

"Uncle Joe loaned me his rifle and set me on a stump in the woodlot north of the creek where we use to spend so much time building forts when we were smaller. I'll never forget that morning. Joe went up along the ridge and sacrificed his whole morning trying to drive deer down the draw past me."

"Well, it worked," Wally said. "He shoved about four or five deer out of that thick stuff up on top. That fork-horn came down the draw at a good run, then stopped about 40 yards below me. I'll never forget it. He had his tail up, looking back over his shoulder with his nostrils flared, steam rising with every breath in the cold air. I shot once and he didn't go more than 40 yards. Joe heard the shot and heard me hollerin', so he came down to help me field-dress the buck. Late that evening we nailed those spindly antlers up beside a big broad set above his old gun rack, and I felt kind of ashamed of my buck."

By now I was really puzzled. But Wally was really on a nostalgia trip, so I passed up the opportunity to make a wise crack and listened.

"That's when Uncle Joe told me about his first buck, and he said he knew I'd bring down a big one someday 'cause I was gonna be a fine hunter. Then we went out on the porch and he showed me where he carved a notch in one side of the porch pillar for every buck he had brought down.. maybe 15 or 20. But what I'll remember most is.. .he took out his old pocket knife and carved a notch on the other side for me and told me he figured it wouldn't be no time 'til I had caught up with him."

Wally leaned back in his chair and put his feet up on the corner of his desk, staring out the window, refusing to look me in the eye as he puffed on his pipe. For a minute I wondered if he was trying to put one over on me, but I've known Wally for a long time and it was clear this was no joking matter... something was bothering him.

"I went back to the old farm to hunt deer last November for the first time in almost 20 years," Wally continued. "There's three times more deer now, but you know that spot where I killed that first buck is about like it always was. I set up a portable tree stand watching that same draw that leads down to the creek and was amazed how little it had changed. Those big white oaks and hickories seemed to be almost the same as I remember them on that November morning back in '65. In fact it was nearly an identical morning, cold and clear, with no wind."

"I guess this sounds crazy," my old friend said, "but I swear it's the truth. That big buck came down that draw just like the fork-horn did so many years back ... he stopped in the same spot and looked back, as if something had spooked him off that ridge. He stood just the same, even the steam rising as he breathed. When I shot, I almost knew I'd find the buck fallen where that first deer had went down.. .and that's where he was, close to the creek, stone dead."

It was quiet for a long time, and I now knew why Wally was so serious ... I just didn't know what to say. Finally he said what I knew he was thinking. "I just know Ol' Joe was there somehow. I'll always feel he had a hand in that hunt ... that's the main reason I wanted the head in my den here."

Then he put down his pipe and stood with his hands in his pockets. He looked me directly in the eye and smiled a bit when he asked me, "Think I've gone off the deep end?"

"No," I said, "but coincidences like that happen ... I wouldn't take it too seriously."

"I wouldn't have," Wally said, "but just after Christmas I had a chance to get by the farm again. I just had to check on something that kept nagging at the back of my mind."

Wally turned to stare out into the falling snow as he finished his story. "On one side of that old cedar post on the porch the notches are still there, pretty much unchanged," Wally said. "But on my side of the pillar ... there's two notches!"

In another room, Wally's two boys were into a noisy fight over something and his wife was threatening to call their father. But I don't think Wally even heard them. Staring out into the darkness, he was a good 200 miles away.

Chapter 17

The Legend of the
Creaking Wagon

I was 13 or 14 years old when grandpa and I spent the night on the gravel bar beneath the high bluff which overlooked the Caviness Eddy. We had our trotlines set and baited, and the campfire was burning down. We had no tents and sleeping bags back then, just an old canvas tarp to use as a lean-to which kept the dew off, and musty old homemade quilts to sleep on. Supper hadn't been much, it never was when you camped with grandpa, just hot beans and weiners out of a can and coffee and bread. But we'd have fried eggs and bacon for breakfast after the trotlines had been run.

We rebaited the lines about midnight, with no fish to take off and not much bait gone. And just afterward I crawled under those quilts bone tired, from seining bait all afternoon. It didn't take much to get me to sleep back then, even on the gravel bars.

Sometime in the night I woke up to hear unusual sounds up high on the bluff ... I was too sleepy to know for sure, but there was a creaking noise, and the faint sound of something which sounded like chains dragging on the rocks. Then I heard what must have been a beaver splashing in the water beneath the high cliff, as I tried to reshape the gravels beneath me, and dozed off again.

I mentioned the unusual sounds the next morning as we ran our trotlines in the cool gray dampness of the river before sunrise, but grandpa was busy landing a pair of nice flatheads and he ignored me. One of the fish was better than 20 pounds. We covered them

121

with our minnow seine and wet burlap bags, then loaded the old john-boat with the rest of our gear. The sun had just cleared the horizon when we got around to breakfast, and I was so hungry I ate three or four eggs and most of the bacon. That's when I mentioned again the sounds in the night, and I couldn't figure grandpa acting like he didn't hear. When we headed downstream about mid-morning, bathed in the bright warmth of the rising sun, I felt great, still excited about the success of our efforts the night before. Still, grandpa seemed a little subdued. He just wasn't as enthusiastic as he usually was when we were on the river, and that was unusual. You didn't often catch a catfish as big as that one we had there in the old johnboat. Well, I didn't anyway. Grandpa did. Shucks, grandpa had caught catfish as big as I was.

Grandpa Dablemont was an exceptional outdoorsman. He had spent his life on the Big Piney; fishing, trapping, gigging, trotlining, building wooden johnboats and guiding. For quite some time, he had a fishing camp on the river.

All his life he had lived without modern conveniences, and he wasn't at all happy about the progressing world I knew ... the coming of licenses and game laws and bag limits were seen by my grandfather as restrictions on his basic freedoms. And as he grew older, the changes he saw didn't make him happy.

In fact, my grandpa could be cantankerous and

hard to get along with. Too often he came right out and told folks what he thought, even when they didn't want to hear it. People who tied up all their time working for other people when they could be outdoors and free were numbskulls, according to his way of seeing things. They were throwing away the best hours and days of their lives just to pay for Frigidaires and Fords and automatic washing machines. To grandpa, that was pure foolishness and he very often said as much. Some folks didn't take well to his opinions.

But they didn't know him like I did. When it was just him and me on the river and the fishing was good, he was a man filled with laughter and stories. He knew everything about the river I wanted to know, including the stories of how the eddies got their names.. .the legends behind Dog's Bluff, the Ritz Rock and Cow Ford and the Dutchman Eddy. And that day, as we left the Caviness Bluff behind us, floating downstream to the Mason Bridge access, he told me the spine-tingling legend of the Caviness Eddy.

Jody Hamilton was a hired hand who worked for a farm family on the Big Piney watershed about 1912, grandpa told me. It was said he was especially close to the family, a young man about his own age, the man's wife and three small children. But the family inherited some money and decided to move far away. They sold the farm, packed all their goods in a new Studebaker wagon, hitched up the horses and headed for a new life somewhere in Oklahoma. That new life didn't include Jody Hamilton. He was left behind after the goodbyes were said ... alone, unemployed and unjustly slighted in his mind. Some said he felt like he was owed money, and others spread rumors that he had a wild crush on the young wife and mother.

Whatever it was, he did some drinking, and then rode after the family, catching up with them on the road only a few miles from the Caviness bluff. According to what he told the law later, there was an argument, and Hamilton seemed to go mad. Nothing else could explain the horror which followed. He shot the husband with one barrel of his shotgun, and then the young mother with the other barrel. The older boy was clubbed with the shotgun, and when the mother, mortally wounded tried to save her children, he broke the stock over her head. He killed the baby of the family by hitting it's head over the wagon wheel. He loaded the family in the wagon, then drove to the Caviness bluff and dumped each body into the river below in the dark of night.

The next day, a Houston, Missouri fisherman by the name of Hiett was fishing at the lower end of the eddy when he hooked something unusual. He yelled to his fishing partners that he had hauled in some child's doll. And then they heard him screaming for help. It was the baby!

Upon his gruesome discovery, a search of the river uncovered the bodies of the remaining family members. The county sheriff and his deputies began to piece together the whole story, and a manhunt began. Jody Hamilton made it as far as the community of Simmons, eight miles south of Houston and almost 20 miles from the Caviness bluff. He admitted everything, and was sentenced to hang on the courthouse square in Houston.

On the day of the hanging, Hamilton sang a song from his scaffold. Grandpa sang a little of it as we floated slowly down the river that morning. "Companions draw nigh, they say I must die ... early the summons has come from on high."

From what grandpa said, Houston had crowds that day like they've never seen since. Literally hundreds upon hundreds of people from all over the surrounding counties came for the weekend, filling the local hotel, and some camping for days just to be there. They were jammed into the courthouse square, with some on rooftops of nearby buildings and others in the limbs of trees to get a better vantage point. And as they looked on, the first attempt to hang Jody Hamilton failed and he dropped all the way to the ground below. Deputies carried him back up on the scaffold feet first with a black hood over his face and his hands tied and they said you could hear him saying, "Turn me around boys, the blood's rushin' to my head." They made some adjustments and the hangman dropped the trapdoor again. That time, Hamilton fell to his death. The body swung beneath the scaffold as ladies prayed and turned their heads and men stood quiet with solemn stares. It was the last hanging to take place in Texas county.

The story told, grandpa was quiet. We paddled on, with only the slurp of the paddle in the water, and the birds singing from the trees around us. The Mason Bridge loomed before us and I was glad.

Finally grandpa spoke again ... "Folks says that late in the night you can still hear the wagon wheels creakin' up on top of that ol' bluff," he said. "An' they say you can hear the wagon chains draggin'. But I don't put no truck in that. Wind blowin' in the pines I reckon."

I didn't look back, but I wondered if grandpa could see the hair on the back of my neck sticking straight out. "I reckon that's what it is," I agreed ..." wind blowing in the pines, maybe."

Many times since then we have paddled through, hunting or fishing on that stretch of the Piney. And I have gazed at the high bluff in broad daylight, letting my imagination paint a picture of that horrible day almost a century in the past. And all along the Piney I have camped on gravel bars where barred owls called as campfire embers died late in the night.

But never, ever, again have I camped on the one that lies beneath the high bluff where the ghost of Jody Hamilton drives a wagon in the night.

CHAPTER 18

The Ghosts of the Dutchman Bottoms

I said I wasn't never gonna write about it. I told myself I'd forget it and in time it would just be like a bad dream, or a Halloween story the old folks had told us boys. But I ain't never gonna forget ... it stays with me like it happened just the other night, and the remembering still brings back the terror.

We were just kids, and kids won't listen. We had been told about the old Dutchman brother's place there in the depths of the hollow that led off the river. We knew about the two that had committed the horrible acts when our grandfathers were boys like us. Folks didn't even give 'em names anymore ... it was just the Dutchman brothers that had done it ... and when the posse went for them, 30 men strong crossing the river on horseback with carbines and pistols to take 'em in come bloodshed or blackness, they say they found the two of 'em hangin' by the neck from the big oak beside the old broken down cabin. But it wasn't the gruesomeness of the hangin' that left such a horrid memory with every man that rode down on them at dusk that day ... it was the uncanny mask of evil that was on the faces of the dead men. In those lifeless stares there was a defiance, and some swore that each of the two bore a horrible grin, as if they had died with the pleasure of knowin' they had denied justice to those who had come to claim it ... to those who had come seeking it for the innocent victims that had made the mistake of passing by too close. The victims who had made the mistake of thinking the Dutchman brothers were men instead of the monsters they were. One here and one there, one in the spring and another in the fall. One a neighbor from across the river, and another a fisherman from the city. One an older man, another just a youth, but each and all of them the same ... unsuspecting prey who died for dollars or for dimes, whatever goods they might carry or coins they might hold in their pockets.

They found the graves in the dark hollow below the cabin, six innocent people who had fallen into the hands of evil. There were no headstones, just six heaps of rocks to show where they had been left, or at least what was left of 'em after they had been hacked and butchered and dragged down the hill. And out of respect for those poor murdered victims, the posse cut the Dutchman brothers down and left them for the coyotes or the buzzards or what would have them, as darkness came on and a big yellow October moon rose slowly over the ridge to the east. No man would ride back there until spring, and when they did, there would be no sign of what had happened. The cabin had burned and the oak was dead, felled by lightning and the wind. But those who told the story said that when it was still in the evening, they thought they could hear shrieks and moans from the hollow beneath the old homesite. Others said they heard something different, a faint, wicked laughter in the darkness around them. And it was a place to stay clear of.

We all knew about it, shucks I had been there during the daylight with my grandpa and had seen the old oak stump and the rock foundation of the cabin. I had seen the six rock graves in the dark hollow, and seein' once was enough. Grandpa said to just float on past it when I was on the river, not to stop and to never camp there ... said it was a place where evil lingered and spirits of horrible things spread like a fog as the darkness came on. But when you're just a kid, nothin' stays with you like it ought to. I'm a grown man now, and I wish I could forget the Halloween night we went there near 35 years ago. I wish I could forget, but I never will, and finally in the telling of it, maybe I can push the awfulness of it away at last.

I was 15, as was Buck and Darrell, my cousins, and Orlis Potts the neighbor boy from the farm up the road was only 14. Orlis had a fair coon hound, and Darrell's other grandpa had two. We'd been hunting coons on the upper end of the Piney most every week-end in October. We'd have never went down there to the Dutchman's eddy if it hadn't been for that darn Jake Kimley. He was a year or two older than us, and lived in a broken down place at the end of the Farley Hill Road, and that was a mile from the river, right across the valley from the Dutchman's place. He had lived with his pa, who was a drunk, and folks said he was a petty thief as well. Jake was too, I reckon. They had to be in order to live. The old man was a moonshiner and got some government money and sold some furs. Jake said his ma had died when he was a baby. Now for a good two weeks, the old man had been gone, and Jake said he never came back from the river after a night of coon-hunting, down across from the Dutchman bottoms. His scroungy old hound came back and that's the dog we took down to the river bottoms where his pa had disappeared.

None of us really figured he had. Some folks said the old man had hopped a train up near Jerome Crossing and went to the city because the sheriff was after him for breakin' into Hankin's country store when he was drunk and stealing a case of pop bottles. Old man Kimley made a little spending money selling pop bottles up town at Richard's Grocery.

But anyway, with Jake callin' us all chicken and saying we could get ten coons down there at the Dutchman bottoms on account of nobody ever would hunt there, we drove Buck's old pickup down through the field almost to the river, and piled up firewood to scare away the spooks. It was Halloween night, and we were too old for trick-or-treatin'. I wish we hadn't been.

Jake had some moonshine ... and cigarettes. He was about half no-account to tell the truth. I knew he had stole those cigarettes or he wouldn't have been tryin' to get us to help smoke 'em. Darrell and Orlis had a swig or two as the fire burned bright and dusk came on. Buck and me said no to it, the danged stuff tasted goshawful bad. ' Course Jake went on about how we was both sissies and chickens, him standin' there with that cigarette danglin' from the

corner of his mouth like some kind of juvenile delin-
quent. If my mom had known I was runnin' with
Jake Kimley and there was moonshine along, I reckon she'd have chewed off her fingernails right down
to the first knuckle. No mom anywhere wanted her
kid to be runnin' with Jake Kimley. Folks all said he
was headed for prison someday.

Dark came on and Buck's hound wouldn't leave
the fire. That's the first sign I had that something
wasn't right. The fog began to set in thick and the
fire faded down to almost nothin' no matter how
much wood we piled on it. My old flashlight started
flickerin' on and off like the connection wasn't right,
and we heard Jake's old dog open up across the river,
in the Dutchman's hollow. I told Jake I wasn't goin'
over there for all the coons on the Big Piney, and Buck
got a good hold on his dog. He said he couldn't figure
why the hound was tremblin' so.

Suddenly there was a quietness, and we all heard
it ... a man laughin' on the hillside above the hollow.
Not loud mind you, and not plain, but a man's laugh,
there wasn't any doubt, and there was wickedness in
the sound of it. Just afterward, we heard Jake's old
hound begin to shriek and howl and yelp as if he were
caught in somethin'. Jake called to him, but the
hound just began to squeal in pain. Somethin' awful
had that dog and he was dyin', you could hear it.

Jake had an old .22 bolt-action rifle and a flashlight, and he headed across the shoal yellin' for his
dog and hollerin' for us to follow him. Not a one of

us moved. I couldn't have ... I was frozen in terror.

We all pleaded for Jake to come back, but he was gone, and I shined my light across the river at the willows where he had disappeared. For a good two or three minutes, there was no sound but the whisper of the flowing shoal and Jake yellin' for his dog. The dog was dead! I knew that, and I remembered thinking that Jake didn't know what we all knew about the Dutchman brothers. I just hoped he'd give it up and come back. You couldn't see his light no more, and then we heard him scream. I won't tell you about those screams, cause you don't want to hear it. But for a full 30 seconds, or maybe more, he screamed and cried and pleaded for us to help him.

Darrell threw more wood on the fire, but it wouldn't burn, and Orlis turned and ran. Then the screams grew to an awful crescendo and ended with a suddenness that made the our skin crawl. Buck yelled for him. "Jake", he yelled in a voice that trembled with fear. "My God, Jake, come back."

We knew Jake wasn't coming back when we heard that faint guttural laughter in the willows across the creek, an evil, horrible laughter, and this time it wasn't on the hillside. It was there across from us, with only the shoal between us. I beat on the side of my flashlight to get it to come back on, and when I did get a beam to shine across the water, there was mostly fog. But just before it went out for the last time, I saw him, only for a second, a man's hulking form just stepping from the willows to quickly fade into the fog at the edge of the river.

Buck had seen him too and we were running' for the pick-up, stumblin' and staggerin' in the dark, fleeing in sheer panic. Somehow we made it, and somehow Buck got the old truck up that hill and out of the woods without wrecking it. Back in town we pleaded with the sheriff to take some men and go try to find Jake.

"Boys, it's Halloween," he said, "we got all we can do to keep up with things tonight without going off down there chasin' around after Jake and his old man, who were just havin' themselves some fun scarin' the pants off you boys."

We all stayed at Buck's place that night, and nobody slept. We kept tryin' to tell each other that the sheriff might be right. That darn Jake may have been out to play a Halloween joke on us and we wanted to believe that. But we had heard his screams for help and we knew down deep inside that there was no joke to what had happened.

Uncle Rob and Orlis Pott's dad and a sheriff's deputy went down there a couple of days after Halloween, and they crossed the river to look for any sign that something other than a practical joke had taken place. They came back saying there was nothing there to make anybody think otherwise.

Jake and his pa were never heard from again and the sheriff always figured they headed somewhere far away just ahead of the law. Orlis Pott's family moved to Iowa a year later and we ain't never heard from him since. My cousin Darrell died four years later in Viet Nam, trying to get to a wounded soldier who was screaming for help when his patrol was pinned down in a Viet Cong ambush. Buck and I talked about it years later and he said he knew Darrell was hearing Jake screaming for help that night in the Dutchman bottoms when he went for that wounded soldier. Our cousin was honored for heroism, finally. But we weren't heroes that night on the river, near 40 years back.

Buck and I know we couldn't have helped Jake and no matter what anyone else says, we know what happened to him that night. We know because ten years ago the two of us went back and crossed the river, still hearing Jake scream like it was yesterday. And back deep in the willows, we found the old rusted barrel of a .22 bolt-action sticking up out of the gravel … the one thing Jake owned and the one thing he would never have left behind.

You can ask folks in those parts about the legend of the Dutchman brothers, and they'll tell you about the ghosts of two murderers that still can be heard laughing above the hollow when the night is dark and the fog lies low and thick. They'll tell you it's all just a big story used to scare the kids on Halloween, but they won't go there.

Because nearly a century ago, a pair of evil brothers did indeed kill people in that hollow in a brutal, bloody manner. There's still a remnant of the old cabin's foundation on the ridge above the river.

136

And sure enough, as most folks will tell you who have visited the deep, dark hollow where the victims lie buried, there are those eight graves marked only with mounds of rocks. You heard me right, and you can see for yourself if you are foolish enough to go there … eight graves now ... not six. Eight graves!

CHAPTER 19

The River Buck

The river was heavy with color, fallen leaves patched along its surface. They moved along slowly, eventually to be swept away by the quiet shoals at the lower end of the small eddy. Cloudy, still and cold, the early morning threatened snow and for an hour I strained my senses to hear and see all that was happening around me.

The smallest bird flitting through the sycamore overhead caught my attention. There was a squirrel scurrying along tree roots protruding from the river bank and a heron winged its way upriver overhead, making an awful squawk as he flew.

I reached a gloved hand up to raise the collar of my coat, but the cold suddenly became insignificant. He had materialized from nothing, as big bucks seem to do. Standing head erect on the right bank of the river, in the very trail that I had scouted days before, a fine buck, with high spreading antlers, eight points at least and maybe more. He seemed reluctant to enter the knee-deep water of the shoal and he shook his antlers vigorously as he lowered his head, apparently oblivious to my presence. His hesitation gave me time. Hidden by the foliage blind on the front of my johnboat, I slipped the knife back and cut the small cord that held my boat to a half submerged root-wad. I was drifting free as the big buck stepped into the water, thirty yards below me.

Nonchalantly, he crossed the shallow part of the stream just above the shoal, head high and alert. My hands trembled as I grasped the bow and nocked arrow on the boat seat before me. It seemed like a dream materializing. The boat floated forward with the current, the blind between me and the big buck now at midstream. I was little more than 20 yards away, waiting for the deer to set foot on the solid ground of the left bank and wondering how close I'd be by then.

The crossing I hunted that morning was as good as any I've ever found along the Big Piney. I knew about it because I had seen deer there often and my grandpa's hunting and trapping partner, Old Bill Stallcup, said it was the finest crossing between Dogs Bluff and Sand Shoals. Deer moving from one watershed to another were channeled to that point, a stretch of shoals separating a large timbered region with little agricultural development from more settled land on the other side of the river where farms were interspersed.

It was Ol' Bill who gave me the idea of hunting that crossing from a boat, hidden with a boatblind. The wooden johnboats we used on the river when I was a youngster were great sneak boats.

My grandfather built the first one back before World War 1 and learned to hide it with boughs of river maple, oak, and willow so that he could sneak up on waterfowl along the river. My dad continued to build the boats and as a youngster I spent weekends with my dad and grandfather hunting the Big Piney from a johnboat.

Stalking with a boat paddle isn't easy, but it is very effective when you have a good blind. When I was small, I remember floating slowly up on flocks of ducks, eagles, wild turkey, and whitetail deer. The bucks that we saw back then couldn't be as big as I remember them, but there were some beauties, pausing before us to drink, or crossing a shallow place just ahead of us. Grandpa said the water held a man's scent, and unless there was a good breeze, the deer never knew you were around, even when close. Just how close you could get began to dawn on me as we once floated past a spike buck watching us not 15 feet away.

The buck watched intently and when we began to talk, he stood for a moment, ears erect, and then walked away. I always wondered if he was a pet or something, but a couple of years later, when I was 17 or 18, I was floating the lower Piney with my cousin, David McNew. At the lower end of an eddy, above a shoal, a small peninsula of ground stuck out into the water. A tree grew from the tip of it and high water had washed driftwood against it several feet high. Before we reached it, I saw two ears over the top of the driftwood. On the other side of the debris, a doe lay at the water's edge, looking back across the river as if watching for a pursuer.

We paddled within five feet of her, neither of us speaking, expecting the deer to bolt. She didn't even act alarmed as she watched us. I passed her, then back-paddled right up to the deer. By then, I didn't want to get any closer. We were looking each other right in the eye.

Then I spoke in a normal tone, "Dave, she must be hurt or something." The deer lay motionless, ears twitching.

"Maybe she's a pet," my cousin returned. Still no reaction from the doe. Gently, I reached forward and touched her flank with a boat paddle. I must have touched the ignition. The doe was on her feet in a frenzy and I nearly left the boat. She kicked rocks and driftwood all over us and was gone in the wink of an eye. She wasn't hurt, nor was she a pet. The deer had never scented us and she was apparently just bewildered at our sudden appearance in the water.

Dave and I told the story around town for awhile and quickly became the butt of the local pool hall jokes. No grizzled old backwoods deer-hunter is going to believe such an occurrence. The old-timers laughed even harder when news spread that I had become a serious bowhunter. In Ozark hill country, deer hunting was a serious business and bowhunters weren't taken seriously at all.

But things were changing drastically. The gun deer season was attracting tremendous numbers of hunters from big cities like St. Louis and Kansas City. Some of them were good hunters but there were plenty who often knew next to nothing about the outdoors, descending on the Ozarks by the droves. The week-long deer season took on a carnival atmosphere and we wanted no part of it. So for me, bowhunting offered the opportunity to hunt deer all through the fall, in solitude. It didn't take long for me to become a fanatic.

Ol' Bill was one of those who laughed at the idea of hunting with a "bow 'n ar" as he called it. But I showed him that with some practice, I had attained reasonable accuracy with my old recurved bow. And I would return to the pool hall to tell him about each close call, and mornings spent watching a bobcat or wild turkeys and squirrels and song birds from my deer stand.

I was in college when I got the idea of hunting that river crossing just before the gun season. I told Bill my plan and he said it sounded good to him. Good enough that he'd volunteer to pick me up at the end of my float for nothing more than a few choice deer steaks and a couple of bucks for gasoline.

And so I struck out at dawn that cold November Saturday morning, with a blind on my johnboat and some heavy rocks in the bow to balance my weight. It took only 45 minutes or so to reach the crossing. The trail on each side of the shoal was deep there. It was marked with the imprints of some big deer. Above that shoal, a root wad lay half submerged in a slow current. I would tie my boat to that root wad and wait. By mid-morning, I would float on and maybe shoot a few ducks with my shotgun, also in the boat in it's case. Should a deer come to the crossing while I waited, I would merely cut the boat loose and let the current move me closer.

I never was a trophy hunter, and probably never will be much of one. I would have been happy to have bagged a doe that morning, as most beginning bowhunters would be. But there isn't a hunter anywhere who isn't capable of getting buck fever when a big set of antlers first comes into view. Thirty or forty minutes after I tied my old johnboat to that root wad, my hands were shaking as I reached for my bow and peered over the blind at that broad-beamed rack, feeling the boat drifting slowly along.

I don't remember drawing and holding on a target. It seemed that the buck would never make the bank and I was moving agonizingly close with the current. I felt sure he would scent me, or become suspicious and bolt and run. But as I remember, he never even focused his attention toward the boat.

When he reached the bank, he didn't pause, and when I rose above the blind, drawing the arrow as I did, he still paid me no heed. I felt certain I was on his heart when I released the arrow and at 15 yards I saw the arrow hit home, angling forward and upward.

I had no chance to nock another arrow. The buck leaped forward, and seemed to collapse over the little hump in the trail where the woodland began. I thought for one ecstatic moment he was down for good, but then I caught sight of him, crashing through the woodland and out of sight.

I pulled my boat to the bank and sank to my knees in disappointment. It seemed the shot had been perfectly placed. Now a tracking job lay before me. The buck may have gone only a hundred yards or he might yet go for a mile.

I secured my boat and hid my shotgun, boat-paddle and hip boots in a drift on the bank. My fingers fumbled at the laces to the leather boots I had brought along. Finally, I grabbed the small pack containing my lunch, rope, and several rags for cleaning the body cavity of a deer.

The blood trail was easy to follow and I was torn between taking it up immediately or giving the deer a chance to lay down and stay. Pushed hard, the buck might go much farther, so far I could never get him back to the boat. But I knew the roads on the river ridges and I'd worry about getting him back when and if I found him.

I chose to follow slowly and that was a mistake I suppose. I had no trouble working the trail slowly up the hollow that came to the river at a right angle. The arrow had to have penetrated well and exited on the other side of the body cavity. Blood marked the trail, easily discernible, but certainly not as heavy as I thought it should be.

The buck soon worked up the right side of the hollow as it became more of a ravine and on top of the ridge he headed through open oak-hickory-pine woodland. The trail was erratic. Apparently the deer was wobbly, though headed in a general northerly course down river. The ridge would feed into another wide, deep hollow, and I figured if the deer made it to the bottom of the hollow, I'd find him there.

But the buck found strength I had not figured on. The blood trail wasn't easy to follow by the time the ridge played out and though I could follow it, it took some close attention.

Apparently that's why I didn't see him at the end of the ridge. I heard him crashing away and caught sight of the white rump, tail down, moving through the timber a good 75 yards ahead. He wasn't moving fast, but he had avoided the downgrade leading into the hollow and turned west, heading away from the river.

I found the place where he had lain, blood thick and clotted. I had been moving slowly, but I decided to let the deer have a chance to lie down again. Maybe I had been pushing him too hard. It was nearly 10:00 a.m. by then so I paused to drink coffee from a plastic thermos bottle and eat a dried-out cinnamon roll. I waited nearly 20 minutes, then again pushed slowly on. I trailed the deer for several hundred yards, amazed that he could still be going against what became a gentle, but steady uphill grade. For stretches now, the trail was becoming hard to follow and then suddenly the blood would appear thicker.

It was after 11:00 a.m. when I came to a small country road where the trail ended in a blotch of blood. For a moment I was bewildered and then the heart-breaking truth hit home. The deer had gone down at last, not 20 yards from the road, and boot prints around the spot were easy to see. A farmer or another hunter had passed by in a pickup, perhaps only minutes before. The tire tracks in the dusty road led away to who-knows-where and with them went my buck.

It's hard to describe the way I felt. I couldn't wait long or follow the road, I had miles of river yet to run. I leaned back against a tree for a moment and looked up into the cold gray sky wondering if it would snow. The whole thing just didn't seem possible. I kept warm hiking back to the river and headed downstream that afternoon, with all the strength I could muster on the paddle.

I killed a pair of mallards late in the afternoon, but let half a dozen woodies wing away out of range because I was moving so fast and spooked them. I arrived at the takeout point at mid-afternoon and Ol' Bill was there waiting. I loaded my boat and my equipment and told him every detail of the entire day.

I'd never get over it, I told him as the old pick-up bucked and bounced up the gravel road leaving the river valley. It was my first buck with a bow and it was hanging in someone else's smokehouse. But it wasn't that so much that grated on me, it was the fact that I hadn't killed the buck quickly. Even with all my efforts and practice with that bow, I wasn't good enough to ensure a clean, quick kill at that close range.

Ol' Bill said he could understand that, no hunter liked the fact that at times game can be crippled and lost. "I've trailed a few bucks I never caught up to," he told me. "Even a rifle won't drop ever' deer in his tracks. I know that, an' it's somethin' a hunter has to accept. You do yer best and you realize there ain't no hospitals in the woods. No deer dies an easy death, whether it's a hunter's bullet or a coyote's teeth or starvin' durin' a hard winter or dyin' of blue-tongue durin' a long hot summer."

I didn't say anything but Ol' Bill knew I was pondering that.

"Don't give up huntin' boy," he told me, "just do your best to be a good hunter.. you won't lose many deer if you'll hunt with a conscience, an' never take a shot you'll regret later."

I didn't quit bowhunting and Ol' Bill was right. I don't ever draw my bow without his words coming back. And what I've enjoyed most about bowhunting over the years really has little to do with the shooting. If you're a bowhunter you understand that.

No, I don't guess I've ever bagged a buck any better than that one that crossed the Big Piney River in November of 1969 in front of my floating blind. It helps a little to know that some Ozark family had fresh venison back then and my buck wasn't wasted.

Heck, I don't blame the guy for stopping and picking up that buck. He couldn't know I was on its trail. But I have to admit I think every now and then about that broad set of antlers. Somewhere they are surely hanging over someone's fireplace and he's telling visitors some tall tale about how he got that buck, back in the winter of '69.

CHAPTER 20

The Ghosts and the
Graveyard Buck

The old Cathcart graveyard wasn't very big, and the rock wall around it was nearly gone, broken down by the years and the elements and the ghosts. At least that's what Ol' Bill believed. He told me when I first started hunting squirrels on that ridge, that the place was haunted. He said it had been ever since the time forty-some years back when the traveling preacher had 'drove out the demons' from a pair of mean-tempered moonshiners at the old church one hot summer night.

Ol' Bill was just a kid at the time, but he said that church folks had talked about how they had heard them demons shriekin' and screamin' all the way down the side of the ridge that hot, dark night...down into the hollow and right into the dark cave that set above the river in the hillside.

The old church was long since gone, burnt down and growed over with vines and thickets. But there still remained that graveyard and a handful of old moss-covered headstones where folks from long past had been laid to rest. Ol' Bill said to me, "Boy, with all the places there is to hunt, I'd as soon look the devil in the eye and call 'im my cousin than to see you hunt there on that graveyard ridge. It's full of haints an' spirits, and them demons roam there when the evenin' comes an' its damp and gray an' still. Don't go there boy, less'n you don't care about leavin'."

I'd just turned 16 that October. Months before, I had took my saved-up money and purchased a recurved fiberglass bow at the local salvage store, an old brown and white one that was chipped and used, but powerful enough that I worked to pull it all the way back. I practiced all summer and got to where I could put an arrow in a pie plate at thirty yards. Ol Bill Stalder and Ol' Jim Splechter, the two best deer hunters amongst the Front Bench Regulars at the pool hall, had laughed at me at first when I told them about the big buck on the graveyard ridge and how I meant to bag him in October, before the gun season even opened. But they were over to Grandpa's one evening while I was practicing and they sobered up when I showed the both of them how I could shoot. I told them about the old tree stand I had found in the big elm, not far from the old graveyard, and how it overlooked a deer trail that came up out of the hollow and along the ridge for aways. That's where I meant to get him, that big buck with the tine that grew down on the left side toward his eye.

Ol' Bill and Ol' Jim knew the place well, they said. They steered clear of it after hearing about the civil war soldier that had been hung from that very elm tree and buried in the old graveyard. They said that long before the demon's had been chased out of the moonshiners, the old soldier's ghost had roamed that ridge, seeking vengeance. The tree stand I had found, they said, had been built by a fellow years before, who thought he would hunt there. But he never came back one late evening, and folks who went to look for him only found an old piece of

broke rope, hanging from a limb of the old elm.

Ol' Jim said that years later they found old bones and boots back in the cave in the hollow below the ridge. He said that folks allowed as how they heard shrieks and moans coming from that hollow, and he had heard them hisself. Ol' Bill said that once years before he had traveled the ridge runnin' a trapline when something chased him the whole length of it, and when he ran past the old elm he saw the silhouette of a hangman's noose against the rising moon. Ol' Bill offered to take me to some of his best hunting spots if I would stay away from that graveyard ridge.

I laughed about it all, and hunted there in October just before Halloween. I never went early, and I never stayed late. I'd go in during the bright light of day and still I noticed it didn't seem like there were any birds singing. That ridge was a still, stark place, and there were always sounds I couldn't identify. But there in the trail that passed the old elm, there were the droppings of that big buck, and nearby a 6-inch cedar tree with all the bark rubbed off, where he had been polishing his antlers.

I spent too much of my time looking toward that old graveyard, and listening for anything down in the hollow. I began to hear the moans and shrieks on occasion. Nothing clear, just one or two every now and then, so low you weren't real sure what you were hearing. But I came to believe they were moans and shrieks all right, made by something unnatural and awful.

And then that last time, I heard the low faint voice, a man's voice down behind the old graveyard, saying something I could barely make out, but it sounded like he was saying … "don't hang me, don't hang me."

Well, I never went back after that night. On Halloween, I hunted out behind my uncle's barn and missed a doe...first time I ever shot at a deer. She was in a thicket for awhile, and then in and then out, and moving all the time. I wish she'd of had a pie plate pasted on her rib cage. Anyway I set there thinking I was glad I hadn't missed that big buck on the graveyard ridge...if there even was a big buck. Maybe he too had just been a ghost of some kind, put there to lure unsuspecting hunters like that one who they never found. I looked at myself as being brave as any 16 year old, but I wouldn't have been there on Halloween for a shot at a deer as big as a moose.

When the gun season opened, I worked at my dad's pool hall. City hunters who came to the Ozarks were too dangerous to get out there amongst.

There were thousands of them pouring into Texas county...thicker than sow-bugs under a wet board and some got drunk and some got shot, and some bagged billy-goats and donkeys. I'd take my bow out again after they all went back to St. Louis and Kansas City, and dad and I would hunt ducks on the Big Piney and things would someday get back

155

to normal, but on that first weekend, most country folks knew to stay out of the woods.

Ol' Bill and Ol' Jim didn't. They hunted way back deep in the woods, and both said the city hunters wouldn't get back there because it was too far from the roads. Sure enough, Bill's son came in the pool hall that afternoon and said I ought to go see the big buck his pa had kilt.

I drove by his house late in the evening, and his old lady (Ol' Bill called her that, I never did) was out beating a faded rug throwed over a clothesline. Hanging from the oak tree was a huge deer with a set of antlers that looked wider than the handlebars on my old bicycle. I saw right off that there was a tine growing down along the left eye.

Ol' Bill was gone, but his old lady (who I called Mrs. Stalder) said that he would be back shortly. I asked her if he had killed that buck way back in the deep woods where the city fellers wouldn't go.

"Aw heck no, he didn't," she said, pausing from whacking that rug. "He kilt 'im up thar where he allus hunts on the graveyard ridge, out'n that ol' tree-house him and Ol' Jim built way years back."

The truth hit me hard! There weren't any ghosts and demons, and there wasn't any civil war soldier, nor was there a missing deer hunter whose bones lay scattered in a cave. Those two old codgers had flim-flammed me, and I had helped with my lively imagination.

Bill denied it, that night at the pool hall. He

said he hunted there cause at his age he just didn't worry about ghosts and demons and such, and he was just naturally braver because he was an old war veteran. He said that every time he hunted there on the graveyard ridge, he expected to either come back with a big buck or not come back at all, done in by the demons of the moonshiners, or hung by the ghost of the civil war soldier and drug off to some dark cave by evil spirits.

With all the old men on the front bench laughing and choking and coughing and stomping and slapping their legs, Ol' Bill said that when he learned I was aiming to hunt deer there out of his old stand, he had been terrible afraid that one of those two things might happen to me.... particularly the former!!

CHAPTER 21

Mr. Magoo's Gobbler

At the first hint of dawn, I headed down the long Ozark mountain ridge. It was little more than a trail, made perhaps a century or more ago by mountain families who traveled by horse and wagon to and from log cabins which they had built in remote creek bottoms. Off the point of the long ridge, about a mile from our camp, there were wild gobblers roosting. They had slept above the green creek bottoms where there were flowering irises and jonquils around rock foundations and partially standing chimneys, all that remained of the old homesteads, except for the aging headstones to mark an occasional grave.

It is the wildest of the Ozark National Forestland in north Arkansas' Big Piney watershed, and getting into it is not the problem. Getting out is a problem. Climbing those mountainsides while carrying a 20-pound gobbler is the task which made such spots mine and mine alone back in those days of the late 1970's.

In the darkness, the walk was a long one. Barred owls calling in the valley beside me didn't arouse any gobblers, it was still too early. I walked alongside the deep crevice in the ridgetop we called 'the bear's den'. I had explored the place often in the light of day. It was filled with big oaks and huge rocks, a great place for black bears to hibernate, and they used it. But the thought of black bears with cubs is not a pleasant thought in the darkness. I passed it quickly.

I relaxed in the first gray light of dawn along the old rock wall at the brink of the ridge. I thought

159

about those timber rattlers we often came across in the fall, but I'd forget about them in April, as much as I could in a situation where I couldn't see much at all. Cool spring mornings keep rattlesnakes inactive, I reminded myself. The wilderness valley below me, where the creek flowed, was shrouded in mist, with green budding treetops sticking up out of the concealing fog. Down there below, one gobbler sent forth his salute to the upcoming new day, and another answered nearby. I developed a strategy as I pitched off the ridgetop, and the gobbler was just below me when I gained a flat woodland bench two-thirds of the way to the bottom.

A turkey hunter can't ask for much more than I had that morning. Within 40 minutes of the time the gobbler left the roost, he came over the edge of the bench 60 or 70 yards away, head stretched high and gawking around for the hen, which existed only in the sweet refrains of a cedar box held shakily in my hands. He eased forward, shook himself and began to peck around in the small growth of May apples springing up in the woodland floor. His head was like a red and white flag. When I called ever so lightly, he raised it high, then bobbed it low, sending forth a lusty gobble which echoed off the rising hillside beside me. And then he strutted for a minute or two, broke out of it and gobbled again. Below us, the other gobbler answered. I called softly again, and the old tom decided it was time to find the hen before the competitor arrived. He came toward me at a steady walk, head high and bright, bobbing through the oaks and hickories and beeches...now 50 yards, now 40, now 30. The gobbler below gobbled again, and my shotgun blast echoed across the valley before my tom could stop to answer.

An hour later I rested on the rock wall, trying to catch my breath, admiring the big gobbler I had bagged. I had intended to spend much of the day in that remote little creek valley. The first rays of the sun were burning away the fog, and you could see the dogwoods beginning to bloom on the rolling hillsides across the way. It had been a perfect day, and nothing could have spoiled it, not even the old Jeep Wagoneer sitting in the wagon trail when I reached it.

I had walked most of a mile from our camp, and he had to drive past it right down the narrow, rugged old trail into the best of the woods, probably because he was some pot-bellied greenhorn who was too lazy to walk.

An old man stood there beside it, something of a comical figure in his oversized camouflaged jacket, a short brimmed camo-hat which was also too large, sitting right down on top of his thick glasses. He looked sort of like Mr. Magoo might look if he went turkey hunting, but he clutched an old shotgun, and stood there beside the Wagoneer looking sort of lost and bewildered.

I figure he was eighty years old, maybe, and he was lonely. He like to talked my leg off, admiring my gobbler and going on about how he use to kill 'em like that over in Oklahoma, and so on and so forth. He said he had rode up there that morning with his son-in-law from Dardanelle, Arkansas, who had went on down the road and just left him there 'cause he was too old to keep up.

He was proud of his shotgun, told me it was an old Browning, probably worth a fortune. It wasn't ... it was just a beat up old pump Remington, with the words stamped into the barrel "made on Browning patent". But what the heck, if the old timer thought it was a Browning, I wasn't gonna tell 'im it wasn't. I bragged on it like I wished I owned one like it.

Back then I lived in Harrison, Arkansas, and wrote a weekly outdoor column for both the Arkansas Democrat and the Springfield News-Leader. The old timer said he read my column every week, and he was really impressed with the idea of meeting an outdoor writer who wrote for a big-time paper like the Democrat. That made me feel better about him. After all, I wasn't sure anyone ever read what I wrote, and it was good to find an admirer, even one as old and dilapidated as this fellow.

He had a couple of half-squashed bacon and egg sandwiches his daughter had made for him, and offered me one. I was plumb ashamed of myself later for eating one of the old man's sand-wiches, but at the time I was too danged hungry to say no. While we were standing there by the old Jeep, I'll be doggone if I didn't hear a gobbler well up the valley from where I had been hunting, back toward camp. The old man said he heard it too, but I don't think he had. Anyway, the tom kept gobbling and I thought what the heck, the old man might get up close enough to have a little excitement with that gobbler.

So we walked up the road aways, and I put him down off behind a small pond overlooking the first bench above the valley. Then I got behind him and began to call. And though I can't hardly believe it myself, the old tom began to move slowly up that hillside. In about 30 or 40 minutes he had finally gained a bench below us where I could see him, gobbling and strutting, lagging along behind three jakes. I don't think the old man saw anything that far away. He sat awfully still though, and now that I think of it, he may have been asleep.

Finally, the jakes headed up toward us, and got out of view in the underbrush along that mountainside, and the old gobbler followed them. Before long, I saw them come over the edge of the bench, and those three jakes were leading the way. Twenty yards behind them was the big tom. Naturally, he'd let them go ahead. That hen wasn't about to mate with a jake when he was there, so why hurry?

And naturally, the old man didn't see the big gobbler. But he came awake when he heard that gobble only 50 or 60 yards below him. He wasn't exactly stealthy at getting that gun barrel around where it needed to be, and had a bad case of buck fever. If the old tom had been close, he would have spooked, sure as the world. But jakes just aren't as wary. The lead one looked as big as a bear when it got 40 yards away and I'll be darned if he didn't blast one.

Excited?!! You never seen nothing like it. I helped him get back up on that old logging road with his jake and he went on like it was the high point in his life. I kinda believe it may have been. He was still shaking 30 minutes later, and I dug my camera out and took pictures. Then it came to me that if I traded him my 20 pound ground-raker for that 16- or 17- pound jake, he could really do some big-time bragging back home. And so I did it, although to this day I can't believe I actually traded a mature gobbler for a jake.

Then I set the camera up on a stump with the timer on and we got a picture of me and him together with that big tom. I got laughed at a little back in camp, but I was never prouder of what I had done in the turkey woods. I just kept seeing that old man's face and hearing him say, "Wait'll my grandkids see this!"

A week later I sent him several pictures, and never heard another thing about it until about November of that year. I got a letter then from his daughter, with some of the ink blurred with tear drops. She said the old-timer had died in his sleep back in late September, and it had took her awhile to write. There was a local newspaper clipping which showed me and the old guy with that turkey, and the caption said that old Horace had killed the big gobbler while hunting with outdoor writer Larry Dablemont.

His daughter said he had never killed a turkey before, and wrote that he had never stopped talking about it all summer. She thanked me, and said that he had told her he wanted to give me his old Browning shotgun, if I could ever get down that way. I told her I had lots of shotguns and that it really wasn't a Browning, and not worth much more than 100 dollars or so. I suggested she pass it on to her son, but she said he was too young and her husband had lots of guns too. She said it was her dad's wish that I had the shotgun, and so when I was down there on the Arkansas River hunting ducks in December, I went by and picked it up and met the family.

Sure enough, her husband was a pot-bellied greenhorn about half obnoxious. I knew he would be, or he wouldn't have been driving a 4WD down in the middle of the woods like that and leaving the old man by hisself. But the lady was nice, and she thanked me and thanked me, and cried and cried and told me again that I must be about half-angel to have done that for her old dad. There for awhile, she had me about ready to cry.

The old gun set in my closet for two years or more, until one fall I met a young boy hunting squirrels on a neighbors place where I was hunting doves. He was about 13 years old, and he showed me his old single-shot shotgun with the stock broke, and wired back together. He reminded me a lot of me at that age, except he was quieter and didn't brag as much about his squirrels as I would have. He said his dad had left him that gun before he run off, and he intended to hunt turkeys with it next spring if his grandpa could take him.

I thought about it for a week before I drove

over to his place with that old Remington pump gun. I asked his mom if I could loan it to him, and she agreed.

The kids face lit up when he held that shotgun. I told him all I could think of about using it safely and practicing with it before he went hunting, and he said maybe his grandpa could take him some. So I thought, well, what the heck, and I told him that I'd take him hunting when the season opened if his mom didn't object. I wanted to be sure he handled that shotgun safely. And I could tell you about that hunt and the old shotgun's continuing adventures. But that's another story.

Before I left, the boy told me that he figured the old shotgun was really valuable, because it said "Browning" on the barrel. I told him it sure enough was, that I had never seen it fired that there wasn't a dead turkey resulting from it.

I suppose he's a grown man today, and I'm sure he still has the old Remington. I don't figure the old man would mind that I didn't keep it. It IS more satisfying to give than to receive. If I didn't know it that day when I lugged that big gobbler up out of that canyon half mad because there was a greenhorn where I normally hunt...well, I know it now.

CHAPTER 22

The Best There
Ever Was

Rambunctious, my old Labrador turned ten years old in the fall of '92. Despite his age, he still wanted to get out there and get 'em as much as ever. But he had been to Canada with us in early October, and it was plain to see that he couldn't do what he wanted to do. The arthritis was getting worse, and his health was failing with age.

In western Missouri, the fall of '92 marked the beginning of the big floods which continued until late summer of '93, and in November of that year, Truman reservoir was about as high as it could get. Water backed way up into crop fields that couldn't be harvested, and into the timbered creeks where the acorn crop had been tremendous. There were thousands and thousands of acres of milo, wheat, popcorn and sunflower standing in water, and by mid-November it looked as if every duck in the Midwest had found the sprawling reservoir.

Truman Lake attracts numbers of duck-hunters who aren't ready to hunt that type of water. It always has, and when the water is low, the duck hunting may not be very good. Sometimes you'll see hunters arrive from out-of-state who heard how good it was a year or two before, and they find the lake at normal stage with just a normal amount of waterfowl. When it's ten or fifteen feet above normal, it can be a duck hunter's paradise. In the fall of '92 it was 20 some feet above normal, and paradise wasn't quite sufficient language to describe it.

Hunters were thick as flies, but most of them congregated in the same areas they always hunted, not far from the nearest boat landing. Over the years

I've noticed that most of those hunters who come regularly have blinds built on their boats which keep them from traveling very far, and make them stick out like a sea-gull on a sand bar. Some use plywood, and some use wire, and they cover that with weeds, or cedar boughs or burlap and go to the same place year after year. Several years back, such a boat blind got too far out in the open water and a winter squall caught them and swamped the top-heavy boat. Three men died.

My boat is made to cover big water, and the blind isn't put in place until I get where I want to hunt. I sometimes take it into areas where no one else can go, and that's what we were doing in the fall of '92. We found ducks way up a small creek about six or eight miles from everyone else, where flooded timber next to a milo field gave ducks a great place to loaf and feed. We found it one Monday afternoon when the weather was calm and cool and the skies clear. With two dozen decoys on the water, we had a limit of nine ducks in about 20 minutes, and took movies the rest of the afternoon.

We planned to return the next morning and hunt another pocket a short distance away... an opening in flooded timber, where it was easy to hide the boat, and the sun would be right for good photos.

There were three of us. Mike Dodson, who I had hunted with for fifteen years or so, is a fire-fighter from Harrison, Arkansas who would rather hunt ducks than eat... and he loves to eat, ducks in particular. Rich Abdoler is a Corps of Engineers Ranger on Truman Lake, who risks his marriage every year to take his vacation during the duck season. As a result, the three of us hunt waterfowl from Canada to Arkansas most years, from late September to mid-January on occasion, and we have become very close friends because of it. There isn't a one of us who wouldn't help the other one kill his limit if the law would allow it. And that became the topic of a rather heated debate that Monday afternoon in November as we gathered to clean ducks and plan for the following morn. It seemed to Rich and me that Mike, who is something of a game hog due to his Arkansas nature, was not nearly as selective as he should have been in his shooting. To be specific, he had touched off a round after, by our figuring, his limit was on the water. Mike denied it, saying that if he had erred at all, it was in helping to bring down a mallard drake which Rich had merely crippled. That didn't set well with Rich, who is sensitive about the fact that he is not nearly as good a wing shot as Mike and I, though he has never formally conceded the fact. Actually, he denies it completely!

For awhile, it appeared that if we hunted the next day at all, it would be in three different areas. Finally, I said that I intended to take photo's while the two of them limited out, and I would load my gun only after Mike had his limit in hand and his gun in his case. And furthermore, should he drop one more duck than the law allowed, I would turn him in to the nearest conservation agent. Mike took offense, and replied that he would take only three shells with him the following day, at which Rich and I scoffed heartily. And that's when the whole idea of the Greater Ozarks Duck

171

Shooting Championship originated.

Finally, we would answer the questions each of us had secretly asked for such a long time.. .was Mike indeed a throbbing gizzard of a game hog? Could Rich actually kill a duck without shooting it in the decoys? Would either of the two hunt with me if I didn't own the boat?

We were there at dawn the next morning, the three of us and old Ram the Labrador. Several thousand ducks left as we arrived, and finally, as shooting hours approached, we had 30 decoys on the water, and layers of ducks above us funneling down into the opening in the timber.

We flipped coins, and Mike won, so he got the first chance. The first flock was his, and he would be allowed only one shot. Rich would be next, and I would shoot last, each of us allowed only one shot per flock. When a limit for each hunter was reached, the champion would be the one who shot the fewest number of shells. The winner would be the undisputed 'best there ever was'. Killing a hen of any species would count as an extra shot, as would any shells used to dispatch cripples. Despite the fact that Mike is a game hog, and Rich has been known to shoot ducks only an inch or so above the water, none of us tolerate the killing of hens. It's a matter of pride. It will happen on occasion, but it's a rare occasion, and never is a hen mallard killed intentionally.

Mike had an easy task. With mallards practically in his lap, he fired once and a greenhead lay belly-up in the blocks not 25 yards away. Rich had only a few minutes to wait, before another flock

172

zeroed in on us and circled the treetops. Half of them settled outside the decoys, but one drake and a pair of hens drifted in on cupped wings near Rich's end of the boat, and the greenhead was a dead duck ... literally.

Ram was beside himself, restrained on a leash to keep him in the boat, and I couldn't stand to see him so tempted without letting him retrieve a duck. We let him go, and the old dog gave it his all, returning with Mike's mallard. We helped him in the boat, and he stood there too tired to shake off the water which poured from his coat, trembling from fatigue. I wouldn't let him go after the other one. Maybe later we could arrange a shallow water retrieve.

My two hunting partners sympathized with the old dog, but wasted no such compassion for me. They took a great deal of satisfaction in the fact that I was under some degree of pressure shooting last. I worked the biggest flock of all, and as I sighted down my gun barrel, there were a half dozen drake mallards hovering over our set. But there were some widgeons in that funneling flock, and I picked out a drake baldpate that was beautifully colored and within range above the mallards. I knew before I pulled the trigger that the shot would be good, and the widgeon tumbled from the skies as the rest of the flock fought for altitude. I had the edge now, with the third duck of my limit, since only two of the three could be mallards back then.

In the next thirty minutes, Mike picked up his "extra" duck by dropping an immature pintail drake that came in with fifteen or twenty mallards. Rich followed with his second drake mallard and when it was my turn, I swung on two drake mallards which swept wide and sailed into range just taking a look at the decoys. I shouldn't have risked it, but I did, and the lead greenhead folded neatly at the gun blast. So far, we had dropped six ducks with six shots. And now, something that had started out as half-hearted competition for the fun of it, was turning into a serious shooting match.

Mike had the upper hand, needing a drake mallard to finish out, and no time to think about missing. With six or seven ducks over the decoys, he carefully chose his last shot, and with a final drake plunging stone dead into the floodwaters before us, he unloaded his gun with a smug look of defiance.

Rich could take no more mallards, and he had to pass up two or three flocks before he had a chance at his third duck. It wasn't an easy shot, but he made it, picking off a drake widgeon as it flared above the decoys behind several mallards which had hit the water briefly and sprang back into flight.   Now we had eight ducks with eight shots, and it was my turn. Despite the cool morning, there were beads of sweat on my forehead. I scarcely heard my comrades calling pleadingly to a new flock, scarcely noticed my trembling Labrador looking anxiously to the skies where red-legged mallards were descending like leaves from a summer whirlwind. It had come down to this, a final shot to determine if I would be able to show my face at Peggy's Restaurant that afternoon, where my hunting partners would be quick to point out that I had ruined a perfect morning on the marsh.

174

If it came to that, I could sit in the pick-up and go without coffee! There was a rush of wings, and mallards all around us. I could hear Mike whispering to Rich, "What's he waiting for?" It was now or never!

I snapped the stock to my shoulder, picked a green head from the descending flock and squeezed the trigger as my barrel crossed his path. In only seconds it seemed, they were gone, dozens of mallards that had been intent on loafing there in the acorn-filled backwaters of the Truman Lake tributary, now hastily retreating from sight toward the distant horizon, scarcely visible through the maze of branches. All of them but one! I have never breathed a bigger sigh of relief... my mallard floated stone dead among the decoys.

We sat there for a moment, savoring the moment, the best of friends once again, having figured out a way to keep Mike honest, with all of us surprised that any of us could have killed three ducks with three shots.

But it was a bittersweet triumph, because we all knew without saying it that it was my old Labrador's last trip. Since retrieving that first duck, he had sat beside me straining at a leash which kept him in the boat while he watched ducks splashing into the decoys less than 30 yards away. For so many years there had been the four of us. You just had to count old Ram. On long trips he had stretched out in the back seat of my extended cab pick-up, knowing that he would be called upon to find the cripples and make the longest of retrieves. All the way to Canada or Nebraska or Iowa, you never knew he was there.

The old chocolate Lab had never been a perfect dog... I don't suppose he would have won any ribbons, and I didn't care. Despite the fact that he couldn't stay put until I sent him, Ram was my dog, and I loved him, and I think Rich and Mike did too. There were many ducks over the years which he retrieved that we would not have found. There were memories of great hunts, times when he found cripples underwater, the day he broke through ice to disappear beneath an undercut bank in pursuit of a crippled mallard. I thought he was a goner that day, but after a full 30 seconds he came back out with the mallard in his mouth.

Ram sat beside my desk when I worked, and from the front porch he watched over my daughters at play when they were young. During the fall he hunted pheasants and ruffed grouse and prairie grouse, ducks and geese. There were so many memories, and now I knew we were down to the very last one.

And so I let him go once more, for one last retrieve, one last duck. He had several on the water to choose from, and he got the easiest one, a drake mallard that had floated out away from the blocks. When he got it, he didn't come right back, he waded out to a little mud flat and just stood there for a moment, catching his wind. Mike and Rich said we ought to go get him, but I stopped them. Ram was enjoying it. He stayed there for awhile, with ducks in the air above him and decoys bobbing ever so slightly in the sun. And he savored the moment, as I was doing, remembering.

We helped him back in the boat, and I guess I never praised him more for so little. It was a great day, a great hunt ... the way it should be for a great dog's last retrieve.

There never was a declared winner in the Greater Ozarks Duck Shooting Championship, by the way. We intended to continue it the next morning, but we hunted a different spot that day, and before we agreed on the shooting order, a flock of ringnecks came whistling in over our blocks and caught us by surprise. As those bluebills often do, they swung out over the lake and circled back for a second look, and three shotguns roared in unison as they returned. Six or seven shotshell hulls hit the floor of the boat, and when the action was over, one ringneck lay on his back, kicking feebly at the sky. Whoever dropped that one blackjack out of that squadron of jets is unarguably the champion duck hunter ... but we have no idea which one of us it was!

I hope that once again this fall we will be trying to determine just which of the three of us is the best there ever was, somewhere where there are backwaters teeming with ducks. I have a great Labrador to hunt with, a grandson of Rambunctious, and the spitting image of the old dog, with lots of spirit, and lots of ability. His grandpa is gone now, he died peacefully one morning in the summer of 1993, and he rests now beneath the oaks and hickories beside the kennel where younger dogs carry on his lineage. With him is the English Setter, Freckles, who was his best friend and pheasant hunting partner, and who died a few months before he did. In his last days, he doddered around my house on arthritic legs and hunted field mice, and I believe he was a happy old dog 'til the very end.

It hurt a great deal to see him go, but I feel lucky to have owned such a companion and to have been rewarded with all those hunts, which some hunters only dream of. And every time a flock of ducks circles high above my decoys, I feel like he's there in spirit, watching it all, still trembling with excitement and anticipation.

Indeed, Ram will live on as long as Mike and Rich and I hunt ducks, and as long as he has grandsons and great grandsons to continue the tradition. And it is fitting that his last trip and his last retrieve took place on that glorious day in the fall of '92, when the hunting was as good as it can get.. .maybe the best there ever was for us. The old dog deserved that kind of a finish, because as far as I'm concerned he really is "the best there ever was."

CHAPTER 23

Stormophobia

On or about midnight a 3-inch rock surrenders beneath my sleeping bag and sinks into the stream bank upon which I have secured my flimsy tent. Either that or my bruised and battered ribs can no longer feel it. I am bone tired after a day of floating. The trotlines are set and baited and cooking utensils and supper items are strewn neatly about in the dark. Fishing gear is comfortably stashed in the old johnboat which has been abandoned on the gravel bar beside glowing embers which are all that remain of a crackling fire earlier in the evening.

It is as quiet and peaceful a setting as you could dream of, the river flowing gently past, no sound except for the rush of water on a nearby shoal, a whippoorwill nearby trying his darndest to get his call perfected, a big bull frog down river bellowing his contentment with a full belly of crayfish, and the faint rumble of thunder upstream. THUNDER!!!

Instantly, my heavy eyelids fly open. My ears alert my slumbering brain to get both legs ready. I lay there for a moment, arguing that the thunder is distant, maybe it'll pass to the north. Fat chance. I can envision a boiling thunderhead with a wicked countenance, a handful of lightning bolts in one hand, a huge bucket of water in the other and a pet tornado tagging along at his heels. He has spotted me from afar.

In a rumbling, growling voice he tells his band of marauders, "There he is boys. We've caught ol' Dablemont on the river again."

But this time I have an option. I have planned well. There is a small cave in the bluff behind me. By the time the thunderstorm gets to me, I'll be wedged in the back of that rock crevice.

Twenty miles away, the thunderhead gives up and circles to the south. "Never mind boys," he tells his troupe. "He got in a hole."

And I sleep fitfully in that cave all night, prepared to leave only when I hear cardinals singing in the morning sunshine. It has always been that way. Great thunderheads roam the Midwest in the spring, searching for my johnboat resting on a gravel bar.

I never actually had a tent in the good old days of my boyhood. I used a big canvas tarpaulin and rigged a sort of lean-to. Staying dry was difficult when we had a heavy dew. It was impossible if it rained. So we always camped close to a cave and retreated to such natural protection when the first rumble of thunder echoed across the river valley.

During one particularly bad storm, I worried about my canvas tarp being blown away in the wind. It possibly would have been, but fortunately a huge sycamore limb had fallen across it to hold it down. It held it down for a week or so as I remember.

Such experiences left a lasting effect on me. Once in my younger days I took a pair of northerners on an Ozark float trip in June and in mid-afternoon dark clouds began to form to the west, with the ominous roll of thunder in the distance. I knew of a big, deep cave nearby with a dry floor, so I secured the boat in a protected spot and we carried our gear up to the cave. One of the men wanted to keep floating, thinking the storm might miss us, and confident that if it didn't we could be at least a mile or so downstream before it got to us. I told him that some ancient Chinese philosopher and wise man had once said that it is better to sit in a cave and look for the storm than to sit in the storm and look for the cave. No Chinese philosopher actually said that but he would have if he had spent much time on the river with me.

I suffer from what is known as stormophobia, a condition not yet discovered by those people who research such things and receive big government grants to come up with those kind of terms. It is similar to clostrophobia (fear of closets) highdrophobia (fear of height) and snakophobia (fear of snakes).

It began when I was rather young. Tom and Roy Morton and I were caught on the river in a terrible storm one Saturday night, sleeping on a musty-smelling mattress in the back of my dad's 1950 pick-up truck, which was then almost as old as we were. I guess, come to think of it, it still is! Anyway, we had trotlines set and supper finished. Supper is a river term for bologna, cheese and mayonnaise on bread. It begins when the campfire is built and ends when you turn in three or four hours later and there are no bananas and twinkies left.

We had the old canvas tarp across the pick-up rack that night, but when that storm blew up and we heard the sirens go off in town, several miles away, we knew we were going to have a hard time staying dry.

So we drove up to Squire Lee's house. Squire Lee looked to be about 100 years old then. He always let us drive through his field to the river where we fished and camped and he was a fine old man in broad daylight. But it is difficult to figure how an old man will act when you begin pounding on his door at midnight. I wasn't altogether sure a blast of buckshot would not greet us, but it was a chance I'd gladly take faced with certain annihilation by wind, lightning and thunder. When he came to the door, I just asked meekly if he had a cellar somewhere, or maybe a small cave big enough for the three of us.

I'll never forget the old man's slow, drawn-out reply, "Boys. . .if yer gon-na die. . yer gon-na die. Now go on back an' let me sleep."

It was his way of telling us that we should let the storm choose who it blows away. That was a bit easier to swallow I suppose at his age. We did end up driving the pick-up into his old barn and we stayed dry while the ferocity of the storm terrorized us.

Tom and I stayed awake, muttering prayers beneath our breath every time a bolt of lightning crashed down within two miles of us. Because of that storm, I had to try to make good on several promises pertaining to how I treated my younger sisters and doing chores around the house for Mom. I think I even paid one of my cousins back a quarter I had cheated him out of and Tom and Roy Wayne and I all three made it to church the following morning, something that didn't happen very often after a Saturday night fishing trip.

Roy slept through that storm and I have never forgiven him. A few years later, camped in a small tent on a river gravel bar, I suffered through a major storm one night with another fishing buddy who snored right through it all, and I haven't liked the guy since. It's very inconsiderate of anyone to sleep through a storm in the presence of a stormophobiac. If he prays, join him. . . if he charges madly into the night in search of a cave, act like you are trying to get there first. This will make him feel some better when you are floating casually down the river the next day soaking up sunshine and listening to the birds sing.

There is nothing I hate worse than someone who gives you those averages. You know what I mean, the guy who says, "Well now, the chances of being hit by lightning is one in a thousand!"

As much as I like to fish with my Uncle Norten, I just can't stand that man in a storm. Half asleep, he always says, "I ain't lookin' for no cave. Your chances of gettin' blown away in a tornado are slimmer than gettin' hit by lightnin'."

Now how's that going to help me feel any better? One night we were camped on the Kings river in Arkansas when a real frog-stranglin', gully-

washin' limb-wrenchin' storm swept down upon us.
I woke up Uncle Norten and said I was heading for
the cave in the bluff behind us. He said to watch for
snakes! Boy what a big help that was. Fifty percent
chance of getting fried by a bolt of lightning or
blown halfway to Kansas against a fifty percent
chance of being snakebitten in the dark. That night
has always stayed with me. To this day, I always tell
somebody who's afraid snakes, "Your chances of
getting snakebitten are slimmer than gettin' hit by
lightnin'."

In the middle of a storm, there are few assur-
ances for a stormophobiac. He is convinced that he
will be in the headlines of the local paper the next
morning. Never lose patience with such a person.
Some years ago when I was just a youngster, my new
wife and I went for a float trip, arranging for my dad
to pick us up at the appointed time. Halfway through
the day a severe storm zeroed in on us and I took
shelter in a nearby cave. It would have been no big
problem had I not stayed in the cave two hours later
than the time Dad had agreed to meet us several
miles downstream. We made it finally and Dad was
fit to be tied. I kept the boat in mid-stream until he
promised he wouldn't really break my neck the
minute he got his hands on me.

I never could really figure out why he'd get so
mad about self-preservation being more important
than punctuality. My wife suggested it was a normal
reaction from a father worried sick about two kids

for whom he had just co-signed a pretty good-sized loan. And it was his boat we had borrowed.

Over the years I've learned to accept the fact that others don't understand this condition. I've learned to live with it. Actually, in other respects I've always considered myself capable of modest bravery.

As a boy I used to sit in history class and day-dream ... there I was in the African veldt, faced with a charging bull rhino. "That's the one all right," I tell my gunbearer behind me, "the one that has killed 264 Watusi warriors in the past two months."

Calmly, I extend my hand. "My rifle," I turn to my gun-bearer. In the corner of my eye I catch a glimpse of him hotfooting across the sands with my government .45-70. I turn to face the rhino. There's two options. I can try to catch up with the gun-bearer, or use the knife. The rhino is 30 yards away. Calmly I grasp the haft of my 14-inch Bowie knife and wait.

Then in math class I would peer across the soft-ball field to Kansas' plains and shut out everything as the daydreaming continued ... I sink into a chair behind a poker table in the Long Branch saloon. "Bring me a half gallon of 'Ol' Injun Fighter' Miss Kitty." I tip my hat to the beautiful redhead who idol-izes me. Darn woman will never give up. It's cool in the saloon and I'm halfway through the half gallon when the deputy charges in, out of breath. "They're comin' fer ya, the whole Jones gang ... 22 of 'em in all."

"Twenty-four," I reply calmly, "I heard they broke out of jail this mornin'. Figgered they'd be headin' this way."

Suddenly the beautiful redhead is beside me. "You can't go out there," she says.

I rise, slug down the remainder of the half-gallon jug, examine my six-shooters coolly and instruct the deputy to evacuate the town. "Sorry, Kitty," I reply. "This is the gang that wiped out that cavalry troop over in Hayes City. Some things a man's just gotta do."

Then in science class, the teacher begins to talk about the elements. She gets around to thunder, lighting, and storms. I begin to daydream again … she's a gorgeous blonde, the local schoolmarm. God knows what those Apaches would have done to her had I not ridden into their camp and rescued her.

But we've left them behind in the swirling dust and now we're resting at a cool spring. She looks into my eyes and says, "I owe you everything."

It's just the two of us. The marauding savages will never catch us now. They have followed in hot pursuit for a hundred miles, maybe two hundred. But no Indian pony could ever keep up with my big black stallion, Thunder … THUNDER!!!!! I look up and see a black cloud sweeping across the plain, jagged lightning stabbing at the earth.

The big stallion is tired, but with one rider he still might outrun the fast approaching tornado. I'm on his back in a flash. "Try to find a cave, lady." I yell over my shoulder as the stallion gallops for the horizon. "There's a storm coming."

CHAPTER 24

Phed up with
Pheasants

Some people say pheasants are hard on good bird dogs. They say you can ruin a good pointing dog by letting him follow the scent of a rooster racing through a cornfield like a laboratory rat through a maze. Pheasants haven't hurt my dogs so much, but they have darned near ruined me.

If you have ever watched that coyote in the cartoons, bent upon catching the roadrunner, you have some idea of how I have hunted pheasants over the years and the result of my efforts. I particularly remember, with a queasy stomach and a tightening of the neck muscles, a December day years ago that I relive in recurring nightmares from time to time.

An Iowa friend of mine had purchased a Draathar, known to some as a German Wirehaired Pointer. He said the idea behind the breed was versatility and not looks. I pointed out to him on numerous occasions that his dog certainly lived up to some of what was expected from her ... she had no looks! But somehow as the dog grew older, she became reasonably proficient at hunting pheasants, and as fate would have it, she had her best day when I had my worst.

It never would have happened had I clung to tradition. Traditionally, I hunted ducks and pheasants with a Smith and Wesson automatic 12-gauge. But some of my friends had commented that it really didn't look right for an outdoor writer to haul out a long-barreled duck gun and a box of three-inch magnums for a day afield in pursuit of pheasants. There was the insinuation that it wasn't sporting to overpower the noble rooster with the same shot and powder one might use on a drake mallard.

To me, comparing a pheasant to a mallard is like comparing a billy goat to an elk. The mallard, after all, is a native American which has earned my respect over the years by coming to decoys the way he is suppose to in accordance with tradition. A mallard will not spur a retriever, run into a hole in the ground or make frequent forays into a barnyard to bully domestic waterfowl. And it always gave me just as much satisfaction to see a rooster pheasant bite the dust at 40 yards as at 25, which is another reason my 12- gauge duck gun occasionally became a 12-gauge pheasant gun. But somehow, I was swayed by the argument that a pheasant deserves a better chance. A better chance my ear!

In the name of sportsmanship, I visited the local gun and pawn shop and was steered toward a beautiful over-and-under 20 gauge made in a Belgium-owned colony of South America. Lefty, the shop owner, said it originally sold new for nearly $1,000 and was owned by a little old lady who had bought it for self defense. It was a steal at $250 and I talked him down to $200.

The following week found me in southern Iowa, hunting pheasants with my friend who owned the Draathaar. It was a cold, clear day and it was necessary to wear a great deal of clothing to keep from freezing to death. Half-frozen, a group of roosters sought heavy cover and sat tight. Half-frozen, I stumbled along behind that dog clutching the 20-gauge on its first hunting trip. It wasn' t long before the dog pointed and staunchly held the bird only a few feet before her nose. It rose with tail-feathers gyrating, cackling defiantly and was so close I could see the terror in his eyes.

I fired the first shot, and watched in disbelief as the pheasant leveled off as if he hadn't felt a thing. When it dawned on me that I had missed, I suppose the rooster was 25 to 30 yards away. I fired round number two, and watched in amazement as the pheasant glided to safety on a distant horizon.

No one likes to miss, but occasionally it happens, and a man has to accept it as part of the hunt. I didn't say a word as I picked up my gun and bore the brunt of my partner's sarcasm.

When I had heard enough, I pointed out that I had shot more rooster pheasants in one season than his dog was likely to point in its lifetime. It was most likely an inaccurate statement, but he couldn't prove it.

Walking into the wind, my face was becoming too numb to talk and my fingers too numb to shoot. Unfortunately, the dog was impervious to the cold and within 15 minutes of the first point, she made another one.

Confidence shaken by my first experience with the new shotgun, I walked in behind her, half hoping the bird was a hen. It wasn't and I fired both barrels with the same result ... a rooster pheasant gliding into a distant cornfield, grinning all the way.

At this point there has to be some disbelievers out there convinced I'm making this up. No one could miss two rooster pheasants flushing within 15 yards of a dog staunchly on point. I wouldn't have believed it either, but I saw it happen from the best possible vantage point.

The worst thing is, I saw it happen a third time about 25 minutes later. It was a different pheasant, but the same gun. It hurts too much to go into it further. What really digs at me is the hours and hours I 've hunted pheasants with that automatic and a model 12 pump-gun that was almost sure death for any pheasant which didn't get away. All the times I 've waded through corn and cockleburs praying for just one solid point on a rooster every eight or nine hours. Just one ringneck rooster in front of a statue-still pointer or setter about 10 yards, with nothing but short grass and sunshine between me and the horizon. And finally it happened that cold December morning in less than an hour, while I clutched a shotgun made in Llama country.

After that third rooster, my hunting partner actually became conciliatory. He helped me look for the gun in the sumac patch where I had thrown it and said he understood that some of those foreign-made shotguns had awfully tight patterns. But then he said that as close as those roosters were, he figured I could have got one out of three with a rock.

I patterned the stupid shotgun later and found that at 30 yards the modified barrel had a pattern about the size of a grapefruit and it shot four or five inches high. I think it is safe to say there will be no South American skeet shooting champions in the immediate future.

I returned the gun to the pickup and dug out my old Smith and Wesson, which I carried for several hours without seeing another rooster. The dog never pointed another bird if I remember right, but if she did I wouldn't remember because she seemed to hunt as far from me as possible from that point on.

We laughed about it later. Well, I didn't so much, but my hunting partner did. He said he knew he'd never see an account of that morning's hunt in print. Now he knows better. And let me say right here that just because a dog makes three points on one trip doesn't mean she's worth a two dollar bill. She eventually grew old and decrepit and I'm still hunting, so that's worth something.

Soon afterward, I developed my own pheasant dog anyway. It was a little English Setter named Freckles. Freckles had her good days and her bad. But I'll never forget the last pheasant she pointed in the winter of '91. We were in Kansas in late January, just after a trip to Iowa. In Iowa, quail season remained open after pheasant season closed. We watched several pheasants fly away that day, wishing the season was still open. A few days later in Kansas, we didn't expect to see any pheasants where we were quail hunting, but Freckles found one and held it with a picture perfect point. It flushed only five or six feet from her nose and, as I had in Iowa a few days before, I followed the rooster with my gun until it disappeared. My partner across the draw was incensed. "Why didn't you shoot?" he asked.

"The season is closed ..." I yelled back, "... isn't it?"

The pheasant season was closed in Iowa, not in Kansas. Freckles looked at me as if to say, "... and I get yelled at!"

One day in northern Missouri a few years ago, Freckles and I were hunting with my good friend Rich Abdoler. Rich is fortunate to have me for a friend, because he is one of those people who hinted that an outdoor writer shouldn't hunt with a 12 gauge. He hunts with a 20 gauge over-and-under S.K.B. that feels like a kid's pellet gun. It probably wouldn't kill a sparrow past 25 yards, but Rich never has to shoot any farther than that.

I've hunted with him on days when the closest rooster I saw flushed 100 yards away and yet he would walk across a permanent pasture and flush two or three from beneath his feet. He is the luckiest man I ever met! Pheasants are drawn to him like metal shavings to a magnet. They flush close to Rich, fly slower and always veer toward wide open spaces where the shooting is easier.

But that day in northern Missouri, Rich had no more luck than I had, because Freckles was doing poorly.. having a bad day if a dog ever had one. I had finally decided to leave her in the pickup for awhile, but Rich interceded. He said he had always heard that if you expected a dog to do better, you had to let the dog make mistakes and learn from them. So I suggested that he take the setter one way while I went the other.

We were scarcely across the fence when Freckles came down solid on point next to a waist-high patch of horse weeds on a little knoll next to a cattle trough. It was obviously not pheasant country, but what the heck, we were close. To my surprise, as we walked past

196

her, two hens flushed to my left and I swung on them instinctively. It was about that time I heard Rich shoot twice. By the time I turned 180 degrees to see what had happened, there was nothing but feathers floating on the breeze. Freckles was bringing back a fat rooster pheasant and another lay stone dead not ten yards beyond the feed trough.

My dog gave Rich the pheasant, and there they were reveling in their good fortune. He was bragging on her and she was wagging her tail as if she had never seen two dead roosters at one time. It was sickening!

Off by myself that afternoon I killed a ringneck which flushed from heavy cover and climbed high enough to clear the tree tops. I led him about six feet and watched him fold, crashing into a thicket on the other side of a shallow creek.

It was one of those corn-belt creeks with only a few inches of water and several feet of mud. The water and mud was at the bottom of an eight foot ditch and the banks were straight up and down.

Freckles came over to see what I had shot at, half expecting to find a squirrel, I imagine. She could obviously see the pheasant just across that muddy ditch, but her attitude was one of indifference. She didn't point it and she didn't intend to get it.

The creek appeared to be nearly uncrossable, due to the steep, muddy banks. It would take little to get down one side, but a miracle to get back up the other. It was like that for two or three hundred yards, except for one log ... a log which had fallen across the chasm and had become a bridge for coons, possums and squirrels. It was about to become a bridge for a pheasant hunter.

Freckles sat there watching, her tongue out, eyes bright, as if expecting to see some kind of spectacle. But I am no dummy. I took off my new Browning featherlight boots and my hunting jacket and laid them beside my gun.

Always an athletic sort, I saw no challenge in crossing a 10-inch log in stocking feet. But some athletic types are light and quick, while others are strong and hefty. I'm hefty! If I had been a foot taller I could have been an offensive lineman,

The log, on the other hand, was not hefty, it was light and quick. When it broke, it happened quick. There is no reason to go into detail about what happened. I eventually wound up clutching my prized pheasant ... cold, wet and muddy, with no log between me and the opposite bank, where boots, jacket and gun waited beside my setter.

At that moment, I didn't care if I ever saw the dog again, but I sure wanted those boots. Downstream a few hundred yards, a country road bridge crossed the creek and it seemed less of a chore to take that route than to spend another ten minutes floundering knee-deep across what amounted to a 15 foot, ice-cold hog wallow.

I made it to the bridge without any major damage to my feet. Somehow or another that doggone setter got across the creek and joined me halfway there. Spattered with black mud, I tender-footed it across the bridge with pheasant in hand just as an old farmer crossed in a beat-up pickup truck. He couldn't just pass with a wave and mind his own business.

Stopping beside me, he allowed as how I had a nice rooster. I thanked him and he continued. "Must've wanted 'im pretty bad," he said. I nodded, hoping he was in a hurry. He wasn't!

"Most folks 'roun' here use a shotgun," he said. There was no getting around it, I had to explain the situation, how I had left my boots and gun and tried to cross on a hollow log. I said nothing about Freckles. I hoped he would think she was a stray.

Pointing to the setter, he left me with some parting advice. "You orta teach that little dog yonder to go fetch 'em."

Rich happened along shortly afterward and with a great deal of sympathy he retrieved my boots while I rested my sore, cold feet. He said he hadn't heard me hollering because he had been hunting on up the creek. He said he had flushed a couple of roosters ... close.

I staggered to my feet and wiped the mud from my eyebrows. "Which way did they fly?" I asked.

The score will never be settled, there will be no forgive and forget. I have met the enemy and he is a rooster pheasant.

CHAPTER 25

Mr. Thompson's Field

A mourning dove, freshly retrieved by a hot, panting Labrador, looks like something regurgitated by a hoot owl. I hunt them for three reasons, to sharpen my shooting eye, to give my young Labradors an idea of what it will be like if we ever see any ducks again, and to get out of whatever work my wife has for me around the house.

Last September I told her I felt compelled to go over to old Mr. Thompson's place to help him with his millet field. I went on to tell her how badly I needed to do some things around the house and how determined I was to get her laundry room fixed up. Finally, I put my head on the dining room table and moaned about how hard it was for me to turn down folks in need.

As I went out the door, my wife was saying something about how her mother had misjudged me. The shotgun and shells were stashed in my pickup, where Gloria never ventures, abhorring the smell of wet dogs. Beau, my six month old pup, and Belle my two year old Lab, were in the back, confined and hidden by a camper shell. I got away with it easily.

It was harder to lie to Mr. Thompson's wife, who hated dove hunters, but not all that hard. After all, Mr. Thompson lied to her all the time.

I arrived at the Thompson farm about 4:00 p.m. There were small flights of doves in the air. There she stood in the lawn, the little old lady who would boil a hunter in oil if she could catch one. Mr. Thompson had already advised me how to get around her.

I introduced myself, took my hat off and commented on how hot it was, adding in the same breath that nothing had been right since the Republicans had taken office. That won her over! Before I could get away, she had me relaxing on the front porch drinking a glass of lemonade while she went looking for a jar of tomato preserves for me to take home.

There was a banty rooster in the front yard, and Belle was trying to get out of the camper, so I figured I needed to wrap up the social amenities and head for the field.

I allowed as how I was there at Mr. Johnson's behest, to wipe out all the starlings raiding the back millet field. She said it was sweet of me to help … she feared the starlings might drive off the doves and quail and she was certainly willing to see anything exterminated that meant harm to doves or quail, including hunters. When I finally escaped, there was only about two hours of shooting time left. I drove my pickup down the farm lane toward the pond at the edge of the grain field.

Past the third gate was the millet field. I got through two of the gates with no problem, but the third one was one of those kinds of gates. Every hunter knows about gates like that … an old farm wire-and-post gate with a wire noose that slips over the end post. Mr. Thompson, twice my age, could close it easily, but I couldn't get the post within six inches of the noose. I strained against it with all my strength wondering if that might be punishment meted out to a hunter who lies to his wife.

With the gate finally closed, I opened the camper shell and watched my Labradors circle the field, scaring up a couple of dozen doves before heading toward the pond. I waited there in a clump of weeds, attracting an early flight of mosquitoes. Beau and Belle cooled off in the pond before taking their places beside me, smelling like the pond, which held eight inches of water, eight inches of algae and 16 inches of mud.

About that time, several doves flitted by and shots were fired (how many is unimportant). A dove flew into a shot pattern and folded into the grain stubble beyond the pond. Belle was on the bird in a minute, closely pursued by Beau. She brought the bird back to me and eventually I got it out of her mouth. Beau was watching and learning.

You could see that he was excited about the aspects of getting one of those birds for himself and there was little doubt in his mind that his master would come through. Actually, I don't subscribe to that baloney about doves being hard to hit. With five or six boxes of shells, I can hit as many doves as quail, probably. For me a limit of doves is as easy as a limit of quail. I don't think I've ever had either.

You can practice in the summer and greatly improve your dove-per-shell ratio, of course. In August I work on my coordination and reflexes by throwing darts at butterflies, or shooting flies off the screen door with a pea shooter. That kind of practice paid off that September afternoon in Mr. Thompson's millet field. When I dropped my second bird, Belle charged from the pile of empty shot-shell hulls to retrieve it. Beau followed but couldn't keep up. In the middle of the field, he conceded defeat and sat down. The pup had decided that if he couldn't outrun Belle he would wait there where the next bird would fall.

It was a heart-rending sight, the young dog so desperately wanting to retrieve a dove for his master. I couldn't help but feel for the little guy. He lay down, head between his paws and eyes skyward, returning only after I threatened to come out there in the field and kick his backside halfway to Kansas.

He would have his chance. I took out a piece of cord and tied one end to Belle's collar. The cord was a bit short, so I tied the other end to my boot laces. Beau would have a chance now.

Belle was a dynamic retriever. Chained to a duck blind, she always waited until I unchained her to go after a fallen duck. But, if the duck blind wasn't set in concrete, it was better to tie her to a tree, and it needed to be a good-sized tree.

She got that way in her youth hunting pheasants with her first owner. I would teach Beau to wait 'til my command, but there would be no changing the way Belle did things, she was set in her ways.

I don't know why I forgot that as I tied her to my boot. I dropped the next dove with one shot, then left my gun behind me as my right leg followed Belle. There are many thoughts that race through a man's head as he is being dragged across a field of millet stubble by his retriever. Foremost among them is the fear of a large, protruding, sharp rock.

Luckily, the rope broke. I had slowed Belle down just enough and Beau got to the dove first. But with the older dog on his heels, Beau headed for the other end of the field.

By the time I got to my gun, both dogs were out

of range—fortunately for them. I had terrible apprehensions of Belle chasing Beau back to Mrs. Thompson's house with that dove in his mouth. Eventually though, Beau circled and headed back to me with his prize, and Belle, much wiser than most folks consider a dog to be, stopped long before she got close and began working on developing that, "I'm no darn good for nothing and I hate myself," look that had saved her fanny before.

As it grew later, I stashed my all-too-few doves and game vest beneath the seat and loaded the Labradors. The gates behind me, I could see Mrs. Thompson standing in her yard with that jar of preserves. I wished desperately that I had checked Beau and Belle for any clinging dove feathers.

She thanked me for my help and I told her we had raised cane with those starlings, leaving vast numbers of the black-hearted rascals as coyote bait. I thought about telling her I had seen a dove hunter skulking in a back forty fence-line and ran the culprit off with the threat of a good thrashing, but I figured maybe I had best not over-do things—she'd be wanting me to come in for pie.

It was just getting dark when I arrived at home. Hiding my camouflaged cap and shirt under the seat with gun and doves, I took Beau and Belle to the kennel. Inside my home, I dropped—near exhaustion— at the kitchen table and groaned like I had been hard at work. My wife, cooking something, never even turned around.

"How many doves did you get?" she asked.

CHAPTER 26

The Lighter Side of Bowhunting

"I just wanted you to know," said the irate voice over the phone, "that stuff you wrote about what to do when you get lost in the woods is pure bunk." The guy calling was a bowhunter and he had read a recent newspaper column in which I had advised hunters about what to do if they were seriously lost. He went on to say that he had followed my advice by firing three times into the air at 15 minute intervals.

"Nobody ever showed up," he said, "and I lost every arrow I had."

Bowhunters are like that. I feel comfortable in pointing out the eccentricities of today's archer because I am one of them, loosely speaking. You can tell a bowhunter rather easily upon close observation. He usually has a little bit of camouflage paint in his hair above the temples, and a painful bow string burn inside the left wrist. He also has a couple of bales of hay in the yard as target background and lost arrows scattered around the lawn from missing those bales of hay. If you have ever smelled buck scent, you can smell a bowhunter across a parking lot from October 'til Christmas.

The most embarrassing things happen to bow hunters. A friend of mine from back home in the hills sat patiently in a tree stand for two weeks of the season without seeing anything but blue jays. Then one day a big wild turkey gobbler walked under his tree and in his anxiety he dropped his arrow. It fell on the gobbler and the bird went three different directions at once.

Another hunter with a tree stand overlooking a farm pond let his eight-year-old son take his B.B. gun and sit in an old barn loft nearby to watch. He wasn't expecting any action that afternoon, but a nice buck appeared and moved steadily toward the pond. As the bow hunter prepared to take a close shot he heard the B.B. gun pop from the barn loft. Apparently the kid made a pretty good shot, judging from the reactions of the vanishing buck. I assume there was a serious discussion between father and son shortly afterward in the barn loft.

It's not so much fun being a bow hunter. Sure, we talk about how wonderful it is to be in the woods alone, to watch those beautiful sunrises. The last beautiful sunrise I saw from my bow stand barely provided enough warmth to keep me from freezing. I sit there and I dream about ol' hat-rack walking under the limb I'm frozen to, but it never happens. The closest anything ever came to my stand was a Sunday morning squirrel hunter in October. Oh yeah, we talk about beautiful sunrises and woodlands awakening to a new day and songbirds lighting on our bows, but we are all out there for something else. I wanna see a deer. I want some venison in the freezer! I want some kind of return on the 40 dollars worth of deer scent I've squirted on every bush within 50 yards of my treestand.

I guess I shouldn't get so upset about this, after all there's always next year. But you young hunters should learn from hunters like me. Stay away from the bow and broadhead. Don't become one of us poor souls found nailing old boards in the fork of a tree in the deep woods of October while our children sit at home without a tree house of their own.

I have always felt guilty about that. My daughters

always wanted a treehouse and I always promised someday I'd get around to it, but I never did. I must have built 50 tree stands for my bowhunting, but not one for my girls. It's probably just as well. Tree houses are dangerous. For that matter so are tree stands. I always think about that when I'm up there about 20 feet, standing on a little platform hardly big enough for both my boots.

And of course I spend a great deal of time thinking in my tree stand, because I spend so little time shooting from it. Even during a very successful season there's plenty of time to think. I don't think about bills or in-laws or politics or things like that. I think about things I enjoy ... how it would feel to be warm again, or how it would feel to draw down on a 15-point buck just once at 15 yards. I think about finding an old wallet with a hundred thousand dollars in it, then returning it to its owner only to find out he died years ago and has no surviving heirs. That may sound far-fetched, but I truly believe it's just as likely to happen as that shot at the 15-point buck.

On occasion I wonder who fashioned the first bow and arrow. I think about those Indians who went out day after day supporting their families with wooden bows and flint points. They didn't have it so bad ... no seasons, no limits, no outside distractions like a job. Of course it is unlikely they had any self-climbing tree stands, but they also weren't bothered with wives who wanted them to stay home and watch the kids or fix something around the teepee.

While it's certain that Indians invented bowhunting in America, it's the white man who perfected it.

We invented tree stands, camouflaged coveralls, buck scent, and string silencers.

Can you imagine what the Indian bowhunter would have thought if he had been handed a bottle of deer scent or skunk oil? What would his reaction have been if he had witnessed a 200 pound modern-day bowhunter working a climbing tree stand up a pine tree?

Of course we have some things in common. Face paint, for instance. And the desire to kill a buck with a 15-point rack. Indians probably sat around campfires several hundred years ago drying their moccasins, reworking chipped broadheads, and lying about the size of the buck they missed a few hours before, just like we do.

There is surely one other thing we had in common with the Indians. The first bowhunters undoubtedly struggled to stay warm. You have to admire their toughness. These deer hunters of the past had no coveralls, knew nothing of holofill or goose down, and never had the opportunity to pull on a pair of waterproof, insulated boots.

Faced with moccasins and little more than a bear-skin jacket for warmth, I would never have left the cave in December or January. My kids would have had to eat acorns until it warmed up.

Every bowhunter knows about the struggle to stay warm on a deer stand. But at least modern bowhunters can grow a beard. Remember that most Indians couldn't grow beards.

I never really had a beard that kept my face very warm. I usually have a beard, now that I'm getting to the age where my face looks better the less of it you can see. But my beard never has been a real good one. There are places where it comes in pretty good and places where it doesn't, much like a lawn suffering from the improper application of fertilizer.

Last fall I had one of the best beards I've ever grown. It was doing a fairly good job keeping my face warm, along with the unseasonably mild November weather, which helped more than anything else.

But one afternoon I stopped by a local restaurant on my way to the deer woods and a particularly obnoxious waitress commented that I had missed a spot or two while shaving. I smiled at her feeble attempt at humor and explained that I was growing a beard and hadn't been at it that long.

With a smirk on her face, she poured a glass of water and commented that she could grow a better beard than the one I had. "Yes ma'am, I'm sure you could," I replied, mustering a smirk of my own. "But then, you're considerably older than I am!" What beard I did have did not keep me from feeling the cold water she accidentally spilled on me!

Nowadays, I explain to those who comment on the scraggly beard protruding from my long unshaven face that Indians could not grow a beard at all. And since I am one-third Indian, I can only grow two-thirds of a beard. Some mathematician told me recently that it was impossible for someone with two parents and four grandparents to be one-third anything. But I don't hang around with mathematicians and school teachers. I hang around with bowhunters and none of them ever questioned that.

In the interest of staying warm, I'd like to close by encouraging glove companies to start selling single gloves. I say this because I have no need of a new pair of gloves. I just need to replace the ones I have lost.

I have several very good gloves which have no mates. Back in the mid 70's I bought a pair of those thin, cloth, brown gloves that cost about 79 cents at the time, and I still have them both! I never came close to losing one of those gloves. But I've bought several pair of gloves in the past few years ranging in cost from 15 to 25 dollars, and I have one of each left.

The good thing is, I can wear one of the right-hand gloves and one of the left-hand gloves and keep my hands warm. The bad thing is, they are not mates and it looks strange to some folks to see a fellow wearing two entirely different gloves. I've never worried much about how I look while hunting, but even a bowhunter can't avoid people forever. And you're inclined to forget you're wearing a pair of gloves that don't match.

Sure enough, last year I happened upon a family looking for a Christmas tree as I hiked back to my pickup. And the smart-aleck little kid pointed out that my gloves didn't match. Before I could say anything his daddy explained that bowhunters often wear mismatched gloves so they blend into their surroundings more efficiently.

I let it go at that. If his dad hadn't bailed me out, I would have said I had a pair at home just like 'em. But everyone has heard that old joke. As I walked away, I heard the mother say, "I'll bet he dressed before daylight!"

CHAPTER 27

The Coon
Swimming Contest

214

Maybe you never heard of the first annual coon swimming contest they held at Boiling Springs in 1965, or maybe it was '66...I can't rightly remember. You probably never heard of it because it was not only the first annual coon swimming contest held on the Big Piney river, it was the last.

The Boiling Springs were the biggest springs on the Big Piney, and I guess from the time the first settlers began to live along the river, the springs were a center point of social activity. There was a crossing there above the picturesque springs, the only one for miles and miles, linking the communities of Success and Roby on the west side with the community of Licking on the east side, pretty good sized villages for the Ozarks of the early to mid-1900's.

At that crossing they held baptizings and singings and church picnics and pie suppers. There had always been a small campground there, and after World War II, somebody put in a little row of cabins just up off the bottoms enough to stay out of the flood waters, and they bought some of my grandpa's wooden john-boats to rent. It got to be a regular resort in the '50's, with a little store there and float trips arranged with guides if you wanted it.

In the early 1960's somebody came up with the idea of a yearly summer get-together which they called the Boiling Springs Picnic. And right off the bat, it was a big success. There was a square dance on Friday night and they had a small carnival come in, and set up a few rides for the little kids, and a ring-toss booth and shooting gallery and that sort of thing. Some local ladies operated a tent-pavilion where you could get hamburgers and sandwiches and sodas and cake and pie and coffee.

Well the whole thing went over bigger than snow at Christmas. Folks just poured in there, the field back to the east of the crossing was so full of cars they had to have help to get 'em all lined up and packed in.

It was the source of good income for me. I got the job of riding the dunking board on Friday nights and Saturday nights. They wanted a sort of smart-aleck kid who would yell taunts at the people who passed and make them mad enough to try to dunk you in the water tank by throwing baseballs at the trigger which held the board in place. I was good at that, since I worked at the pool hall up in Houston, and had made lots of enemies by the time I was 16 years old. I'd holler things at young fellows who passed, like "Hey goofball, does bein' cross-eyed affect your throwin'?"

When the night was over, I'd get 1/4 of the proceeds, and some nights it would be as much as 8 or 10 dollars. When you consider that each thrower got 3 balls for a quarter, you realize how good I was at being obnoxious and rude for just a youngster, and how wet I stayed. The first year I was away in college, I returned home for the picnic and made 15 dollars on Saturday night alone. The guy that sold the chances kept hollerin', "Come on up here and see if you can dunk a gen-oo-ine college boy." No farmer with an eighth grade education could pass that up. Around the Big Piney country, the only thing worse than a college boy was a revenooer. Sometimes late on a Friday or Saturday night when all the families had gone home and the rowdies were drinking too much home brew, that wire cage around my tank was the safest place to be. Every now and then some good ol' local boy with very little moonshine left in his jug would just lose control and start chunkin' fastballs at me behind that wire screen.

As time went on, they began to develop contests for Saturday and Sunday afternoons. One of the big events was a boat paddling contest, in which two entrants paid a dollar apiece to paddle one of the johnboats from the low water bridge downstream 200 yards around a buoy and then back again. The best time at the end of the weekend won a trophy. There was quite a bit of current, and it was more work than it was worth. Still, they had that boat going all the time, once the word got out that Grandpa and I were barred from entering. Nobody had a chance paddling against Grandpa, the very best of the Big Piney rivermen.

There were also horse-shoe pitching tournaments and sack races and terrapin races and, baking contests and I don't know what all. The organizers of the event planned some big things that never worked out. There was the idea of a beauty contest, for one. But no matter who would have won that beauty contest, the judges would have been in danger of being set upon by the relatives of the losers.

And then finally they had that big idea of a coon-dog contest. You've probably seen how they drag a pet coon in a cage across a body of water and let the hound swim after it, then declare the fastest time the winner. There was a lot of that went on back then, and still is I reckon. But in the Boiling Springs area coon hounds were thicker than flies on a week-dead carp, and when they had that Saturday afternoon contest it about wrecked the whole picnic. Seems like everyone brought a coon hound, but the widow schoolteacher and I think she may have borrowed one. The Saturday morning horserace was turned into a rodeo by a half dozen loose hounds, and Lumas Moore swore that he lost the horseshoe pitching championship only because an airborne, ringer-bound horseshoe hit Ed Cantrell's bluetick hound as he bolted across the horseshoe grounds.

There were complaints from some of the ladies about the way hounds have of greeting one another, and the kitchen pavilion said proceeds dropped because four hounds, tied to a tree much of the afternoon, slobbered so bad with the aroma of hamburgers wafting past their nose that it ruined everyone's appetite. The whole weekend, somebody was stepping in something here and there, and there was a big to-do over Hobart Gentry's redbone bolting into the midst of the terrapin race and trying his darndest to eat the lead turtle, which was a pet of the little McElroy girl from Bucyrus.

There would be no more coonhounds at the Boiling Springs picnic. But why not a coon swimming contest? Lots of the coon hunters had coons they trained their dogs with, and several farm youngsters had pet coons as well. So the idea was, they'd turn loose each coon, one at a time on one side of the river, and time how long it took him to swim to the other side. The fastest coon would win $25, and next fastest got $15. I know it sounds a little silly, but you've got to remember that free entertainment is hard to find.

Most of the coon hunters who brought their dog-training coons turned them over to their kids, so it became mostly a contest for the youngsters, except for old Monroe Magruder, the orneriest cuss in the county. His coon was a skinny, long-legged ridge-runner held captive in a chicken wire cage, and he was wilder than a March hare. Monroe felt he had that prize money cinched.

There were strong challengers though. Elrod Shingleford from Hog Crick had a strong, blond she-coon, and Josh Mooney had a young corn-fed male folks said took to water better'n most.

My cousin's coon, Lefty, was a fine thief, but no swimmer. He had no peer at lifting jewelry or stealing eggs from the henhouse. He was high on finesse, but he frowned on physical activity.

The contest was half over when Monroe's ridge-runner came up. That wild-eyed, long-legged coon hit the water and set forth like he was out for a Saturday afternoon dip. I swear, I thought he'd flip over on his back and float awhile at the pace he was going.

Monroe had bet all his moonshine money on that young boar coon, and he began to cuss and threaten him with a gusto that drove most of the ladies back to the terrapin race.

More than a hundred folks on that riverbank saw Monroe's coon reach mid-stream, then mysteriously sink from sight like he was diving for a crawdad. When he finally popped up, he wasn't headed for the finish line of the opposite bank. He was headed downstream with vigor renewed by a taste of freedom.

A sudden, spontaneous cheer went up from all but one of the onlookers. Now here was a coon with fortitude and the crowd was with him. Everyone was running down the bank through a jungle of brush, cheering and yelling for the coon, which had developed a fine stroke.

Monroe was yelling for his oldest boy Rube to get in and get that coon. Rube was tryin' his best to act like he wanted to. You could see the younger McGruder head for the bank like he was about to dive right in, then veer away like he was waiting for a better spot further down the bank.

The ridge-runner turned it on now. Johnny Weissmuller would have admired that coon. Ol' big-bellied Monroe McGruder wasn't even close, but he yelled ahead that he'd give a $10 bill to anybody who'd drag that traitor of a coon out on dry ground.

Thurman Hoyt's eldest boy, Amil, was leading the crowd of cheering onlookers down the bank and for a $10 bill he'd jump in a Black Swamp after a bull alligator. Previously that day Amil had gotten the better of a half jug of Monroe's moonshine, or vice versa.

Amil saw his chance to be a hero, with lots of folks looking on, so he went all out and dived head-long. The water was only about two feet deep with a mud bottom and he sort of stuck where he hit for a minute, then gained his feet and went after the run-away coon. This was the high point of the day. Nearly a hundred panting, sweating observers lined both banks, cheering the coon and booing Amil.

The coon didn't need any help. Amil caught him alright, but the current carried both into a sudden dropoff. I couldn't see much from my place toward the rear of the crowd, but I could tell Amil was sobering up in a hurry. When that coon latched onto his ear and pushed his head under for the third time, Amil made for the bank convinced there were easier ways to make ten bucks.

The crowd was whistling and cheering now as nearly everyone sent forth a salute to the newly emancipated coon. He disappeared around the bend, still going strong, and was never seen again. Later Amil Hoyt was treated for a torn ear and Rube McGruder was whipped for not catching his Pa's coon. Later on that day, Monroe McGruder was likewise flailed for not paying his bets and the '67

221

picnic and 1st annual coon swimming race earned its place in history.

Amil Hoyt is an old man now and his left ear is still disfigured, much to his delight -- a tribute to his act of heroism, and a topic of conversation. Amil used that to get a job at the pallet mill at Roby a year or so later, and he worked up in the company and retired. Monroe McGruder passed on some time back, but his boy Rube still has a hound or two and hunts coons just for the fun of it.

The ridge-runner is a legend now. Word is he sired a new breed of slick-haired swimmers that delight in luring hounds into the deep dark waters of the lower Big Piney. Folks talked about his freedom flight for many years and how smart he was to escape that way. But I don't reckon any coon is all that smart, they just naturally take to swimming.

The Boiling Springs picnic is long past and forgotten now, but the bridge is still there and so are the springs. Those of us who were kids back in those good old days can still cross there and stop and close our eyes and see it all yet today, just like it was 40 years ago. I can hear the square dancers and smell the hamburgers and feel the cold water in that dunking booth. And it comes to me then that I was one of the few people in this world that actually observed a wild coon swimming contest. That's got to be worth something!

CHAPTER 28
The Great Flock

In the warm sunshine of mid-morning the Great Flock, some 200 strong, approached the Ozark mountains, 1200 feet above the highest hill.

At the front of the formation, leading in a northerly course, was the old gander, veteran of a dozen spring flights. Just behind and to his right was his young son, returning to his hatching place after his first winter in the deep south.

"I hope you don't mind all these questions father," the youngster said once again, "but I just can't remember much of this country ... last fall seems so long ago."

"I much prefer your questions over the complaining of some of the other members of the flock," the old goose answered. "Some of our brethren would stop at every farm pond, I do believe. If I listened to them we'd be 'til mid-summer arriving at the great northern prairie."

"Why must we go so far, father?" the young goose asked, "That lake ahead seems so inviting."

"Ah yes, it's pretty and blue," was the reply, "but there's so little there to eat. These Ozark lakes are without grain and deep. There is some grass at times, but most of the shores are rocky and barren."

"Have you ever stopped there?" the younger goose asked.

"Once in a great fog I spent a few days there," his father answered. "A nice place to visit, but I wouldn't want to live there."

"Mother says some of her friends have spent a

summer here."

"That's true. Mostly older geese, retired honkers I suppose," the great leader said. "But if we were meant to nest here we would be called Ozark honkers instead of Canada honkers."

The young goose pondered that as they passed over the sparkling lake below, "Look," he said, craning his neck to get a better view. "There's some of those creatures again, the ones you call ..."

"Man," the old gander interrupted. "There are some of them scattered everywhere, but mostly they live in groups in places where the air smells bad and the water isn't fit to sit in overnight."

"Are there many of them?"

"There are far too many in those places," the old goose said with something of a smile. "Their numbers are so great they darken the ground."

"My that's poetic," the younger goose sighed.

They flew on into the afternoon, the older goose pointing out landmarks to the younger son. "I don't know if I can remember all these landmarks," the young goose sighed.

"Well, that's not so important. Men change them quite often anyway. Any sensible goose knows which way is north. Pass the word back that we'll climb to 2,000 feet soon. There's a city ahead and the air is foul under a quarter mile."

"Why do men congregate in places such as that?" the young goose asked.

"Most have no choice," the lead honker

answered with a sigh, "Men have never been satisfied. With us it is the same year after year because we are content and satisfied with the earth as God made it. But men must keep improving things. So each year the water is dirtier, the air smells a little worse. Strangely, as he makes things better, he has more problems. When he really gets things the way he wants them, he may not be able to survive."

Hours later the great flock swept over the Missouri refuge known as Shell-Osage. "It looks inviting," the young goose said. "Part of the flock wants to stop here."

"Some probably will," the old goose answered, "but the wind is behind us and I have a schedule to keep. Besides, there are too many snow geese stopping there and I do get sick of hearing how fine Texas was over the winter."

"Yep," said the young goose craning his neck to look back, "there goes the guy who has been doing all the honking with a dozen or so of his friends."

"He wants to be a leader badly," the older goose said, neither looking nor missing a windbeat. "Such youngsters see leadership as a prestigious right when it is in reality a responsibility. Remember my son to be always as conscious of your responsibilities as your rights. Those detractors will be late arriving at the great northern prairie, or maybe they'll try to make up lost time in a heavy fog some night and not make it at all. If they do make it, you can bet that next fall many of them will be killed by hunters, if they continue to follow him."

The young goose shuddered. "I am learning to hate those hunters." he said.

"You shouldn't," the old gander said. "We would find few places to nest, and little water in the great northern prairie if it were not for them. They treasure us highly I suppose and you'll find that the very places they hunt have areas where we are never molested, and food is plentiful."

"Men are only predators like the fox and bobcat and those darn Louisiana alligators," he continued. "Of course men aren't nearly as effective as alligators! The ones who we all have to fear are the men who destroy the land, who selfishly mar it for their own immediate purposes. They turn the soil barren and black in the winter and take away the clean water in the summer. They spread poison substances that harm all life, even mankind. Those are the ones to fear son, men driven by greed. Greed is a thing known to no other living creature, only man."

"In time," he sighed, "it may destroy man. We can only hope the Great Creator will keep man's greed from destroying all living things everywhere."

"Are there men everywhere father?" the young goose asked as the sun began to set.

"I think everywhere," the old goose answered. "At least they are everywhere I have been, and I have been everywhere, I think."

They forged on, a long wavering string silhouetted against the sky, colored magnificently by the sunset. In the dusky silence of early spring, you might hear the young goose saying, "Gee father, you have been everywhere, you must know everything."

And with a tired sigh the old leader of the Great Flock answers, "No son, I have been everywhere, but it is your mother who knows everything."

Months later, at the end of a wonderful summer, the Great Flock rests on a Canadian mud flat. The leader of the Great Flock and his two lieutenants are talking of the long migration to come.

"It's the same every fall," the old gander says. "The youngsters can't wait to get started and the oldsters complain that it's too early. Then, when we get going, I've got one group wanting to winter in Wisconsin and another wanting to get a look at Louisiana."

"It would seem," said one of the associates, "that a leader is chosen not so much to listen to and to follow, but to bicker with and blame."

"Those of us who lead are expected to have all the answers, to know everything," the old leader said, watching a group of younger geese making practice flights over the lake. "But if I had known much at all, I wouldn't have got myself in this situation."

"You'll feel better when we get started," his comrade said. "It's been a short summer and I think the weather has all of us a bit edgy. It would be nice if we could tell just when that first blizzard is going to hit. Then we could take it easy and leave a few days ahead of it."

"A couple of years ago I could just feel winter in my bones," said the leader, "so we left early and flew non-stop to the big river where the cornfields end. A month later a pair of independents flew in and said they'd just left the north country and it was still like summer. My wife honked at me for three days about that!"

"I had an old uncle who claimed he could tell the coming weather by watching men," one old gander ventured. "Seems they have some built-in system, or something, but anyway he said he could tell what was coming by watching a group of humans. Of course he got a little too preoccupied with his study and was nearly blasted by a pair of men whom he had thought to be hibernating in a submerged box at the height of a blizzard."

"I've heard that men know how to tell what the weather is to be," said the leader, "but it can't be true of them all. I know of places to the north where there are large numbers of men, and if they know anything about predicting the weather they would have been gone years ago."

"They are indeed strange," one old honker reflected. "I have watched them sometimes as we flew over. It's strange the feeling you get at times, kind of makes you want to just forget everything and stay with them!"

"I guess they have no worries," said the other comrade. "They don't have to worry about going south one day and north the next and they never have to worry about food. They eat anything that they can get close to."

"I've often wondered what eats men," said one lieutenant. "They too are hunted in cornfields, you know."

The great leader was puzzled by that. "Hunted by what?" he asked.

"I'm not sure," said the other old honker, "but I've seen several man-decoys in small cornfields. They were made out of straw, mostly."

"I don't know what would hunt men," said the great leader, "but I've seen those decoys myself. Could be it's something used by the males to attract mates."

"I understand they mate for life, you know," the other gander said. "Goes to show they are a bit like us, I suppose … somewhat intelligent."

"Humph!" said the other lieutenant. "Intelligence has nothing to do with it. After all, why shouldn't they mate for life? The females all look exactly alike!"

OTHER BOOKS BY LARRY DABLEMONT:

Ain't No Such Animal
... and other stories from the Ozarks hills

Ridge-Runner
From the Big Piney to the Battle of the Bulge

Greatest Wild Gobblers
Lessons Learned from Old Timers and Old Toms

The Front Bench Regulars
Wit and Wisdom from Back Home in the Hills

Rivers to Run
Sycamores, Swift-water, and Smallmouth Bass

Recollections of an Old-Fashioned Angler
Angling Experiences and Adventures

Memories from a Misty Morning Marsh
... a duck hunter's collection

TO VIEW ALL OF LARRY DABLEMONT'S BOOKS VISIT:
www.larrydablemont.com

OR WRITE TO:

Lightnin' Ridge Books
Box 22
Bolivar • MO 65613

234